The Thinking Tree

ALL ABOUT
OCEANS

Marine Biology Handbook

HOMESCHOOLING
JOURNAL

By: Anna Kidalova, Notika Pashinko
& Sarah Janisse Brown

We use the Dyslexie Font by Christian Boer

The Thinking Tree Publishing Company, LLC

FUNSCHOOLINGBOOKS.COM

Name:

This Curriculum Includes:

- Science

- Geography

- Art and Drawing

- Documentaries

- Research & Library Skills

- Audio Books

- Cursive Writing

- Copywork

- Reading and Spelling

- Creative Writing

- Logic Games

- Hidden Pictures

- Poetry by Homeschooling Families

INSTRUCTIONS

CHOOSE YOUR TOPICS!

What do you want to know about Oceans

and inhabitants of the ocean?

Draw FIVE things you are curious about:

ACTION STEPS:

1. Go to the library or bookstore.

2. Bring home a stack of at least FIVE interesting books about these topics.

3. Choose some that have diagrams, instructions and illustrations.

SCHOOL SUPPLIES NEEDED:

Pencils, Colored Pencils & Gel Pens.

You will find a Creative Writing Section in the back of this book! Use it anytime!

GO TO THE LIBRARY AND CHOOSE FIVE BOOKS TO USE AS SCHOOL BOOKS!

1. Write down the titles on each book cover below.

2. Keep your stack of books in a safe place so you can read a few pages from your books daily.

3. Ask your mom or teacher how many pages to do each day in this Journal. Five to eight pages is normal for kids your age.

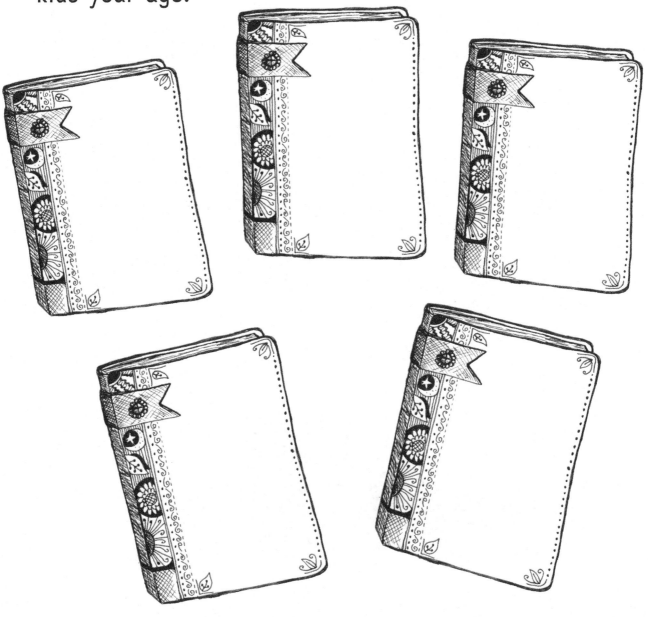

You may choose new books any time.

Flip to the back for more book pages.

Keep all your books in a basket with your pens and pencils.

Have a snack before you start working in this journal.

PICK OUT NEW BOOKS ANYTIME!

DRAW THE COVERS HERE:

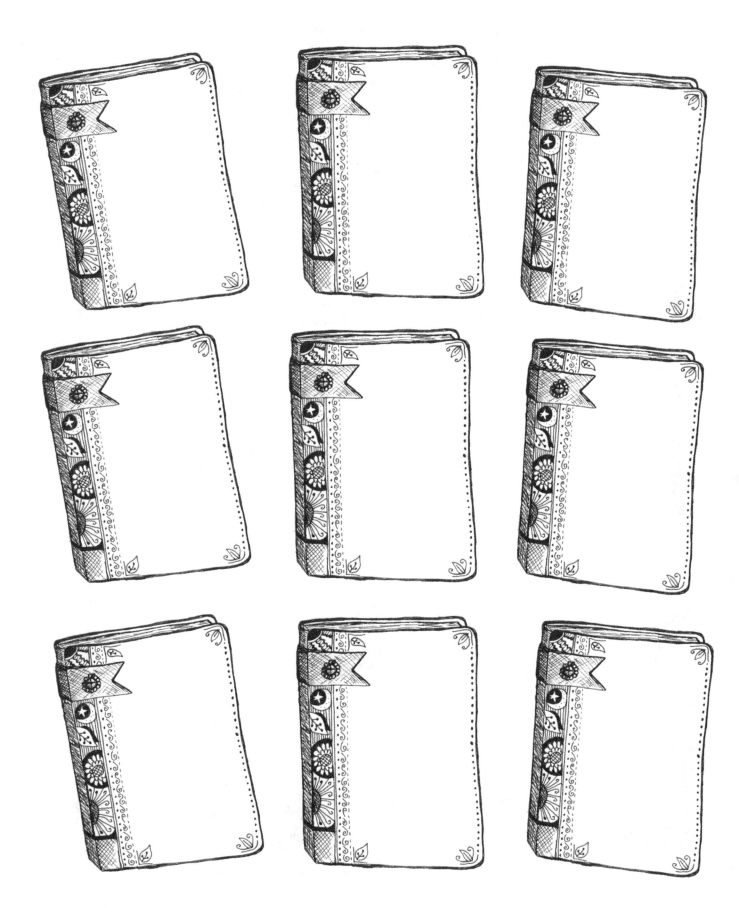

LEARNING TOOLS

My List of Websites & Research Materials:

_____

_____

_____

_____

_____

_____

_____

_____

_____

_____

_____

_____

_____

_____

The Arctic Ocean

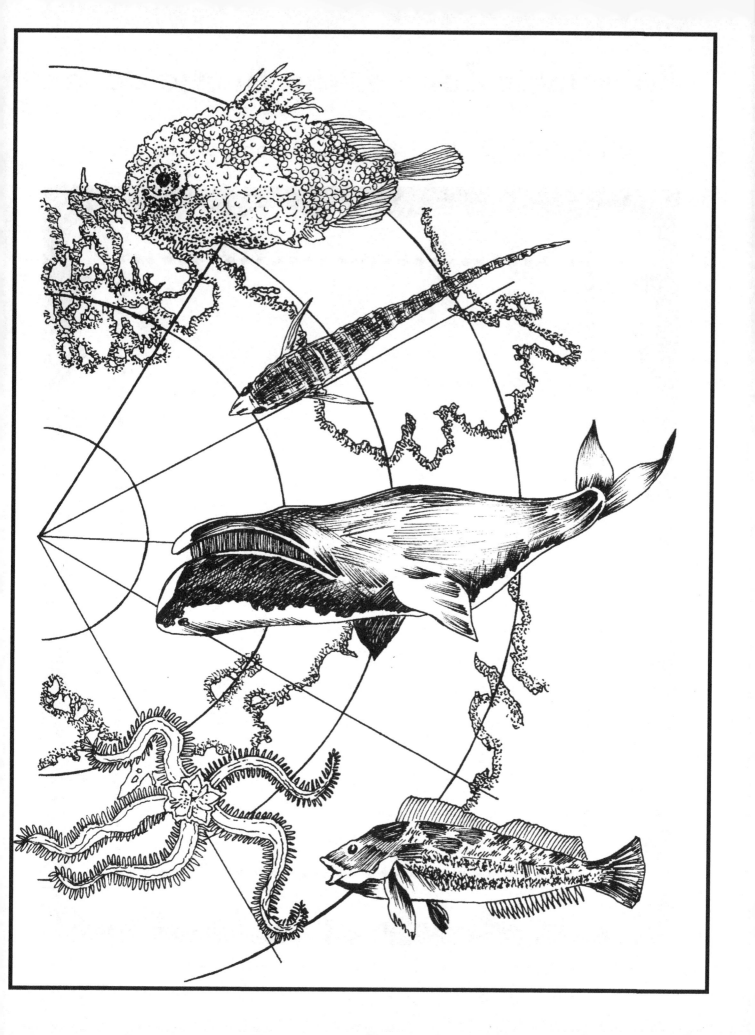

Epipelagic Zone of the Arctic Ocean

Write 3 things about epipelagic zone of the ocean

Find creatures that are hidden in the picture

ARCTIC OCEAN

BY STEPHANIE JACOBS

Artic Ocean,
ice adrift.
Polar bears, jellyfish, orcas exist.
Arctic Ocean,
sea life galore,
benthos found on the ocean floor.
Narwhals, belugas, humpback whales,
joyfully, happily throwing their tails.
Arctic Ocean,
seals all around,
harp seals, spotted seals, ringed seals abound.
Arctic Ocean,
bitterly cold,
a wondrous place for all to behold.

REPLACE THE ADJECTIVES AND VERBS
TO MAKE A WHOLE NEW POEM!

Add artwork to the page.

Artic Ocean,
ice adrift.
Polar bears, jellyfish, orcas exist.
Arctic Ocean,
sea life galore,
benthos _____ on the ocean floor.
Narwhals, belugas, humpback whales,
_____, _____ throwing their tails.
Arctic Ocean,
seals all around,
harp seals, spotted seals, ringed seals abound.
Arctic Ocean,
bitterly _____,
a _____ place for all to behold.

ANIMAL FACTS
SPINY DOGFISH

WRITE DOWN THREE FACTS ABOUT THIS ANIMAL:

1._____

_____

2._____

_____

3._____

_____

RESEARCH & DISCOVERIES

USE LIBRARY BOOKS, ENCYCLOPEDIAS OR THE INTERNET TO LEARN MORE.

Color the parts of the world where this animal lives.

DRAW MY HOME	DRAW MY FOOD	DRAW MY ENEMIES

WHAT'S IN A NAME?

BY NORI HOBBS

Clownfish, lionfish,
so many weirdly named fish.
Razorfish, trumpetfish,
so many that I cannot
go through the list.
Squirrelfish, lemon sweetlips,
dog snapper, schoolmaster,

who decides all of this?

REPLACE THE ADJECTIVES AND VERBS
TO MAKE A WHOLE NEW POEM!

Add artwork to the page.

Clownfish, lionfish,
so many _____ named fish.
Razorfish, trumpetfish,
so many that I cannot
go through the list.
Squirrelfish, lemon sweetlips,
dog snapper, schoolmaster,

who _____ all of this?

Today I will
read for

15 30 45 60

MINUTES

Ask your teacher to help
you decide how many
books to read from each
day. #_____

READING TIME

Write and draw about
what you are reading.

DRAWING TIME

Copy a picture from any of your books.

ANIMAL FACTS
BOWHEAD WHALE

WRITE DOWN THREE FACTS ABOUT THIS ANIMAL:

1._____

_____

2._____

_____

3._____

_____

RESEARCH & DISCOVERIES

USE LIBRARY BOOKS, ENCYCLOPEDIAS OR THE INTERNET TO LEARN MORE.

Color the parts of the world where this animal lives.

DRAW MY HOME	DRAW MY FOOD	DRAW MY ENEMIES

WAVES

BY ANITA GRACE KLAUSE

Waves
Playful, Mighty
Foaming, Rolling, Unyielding
Nature's greatest roller coaster
Surf

REPLACE THE ADJECTIVES AND VERBS TO MAKE A WHOLE NEW POEM!

Add artwork to the page.

Waves

_____, Mighty

_____, Rolling, _____

Nature's _____roller coaster

Surf

SPELLING TIME

Pick a Letter _____

Look in your homeschooling books for

words that start with this letter.

Write ten spelling words.

1._____

2._____

3._____

4._____

5._____

6._____

7._____

8._____

9._____

10._____

MOVIE TIME

Watch a video about the ocean or ocean creatures!

TITLE:_____

Draw Your Favorite Scenes:

RATING:

m

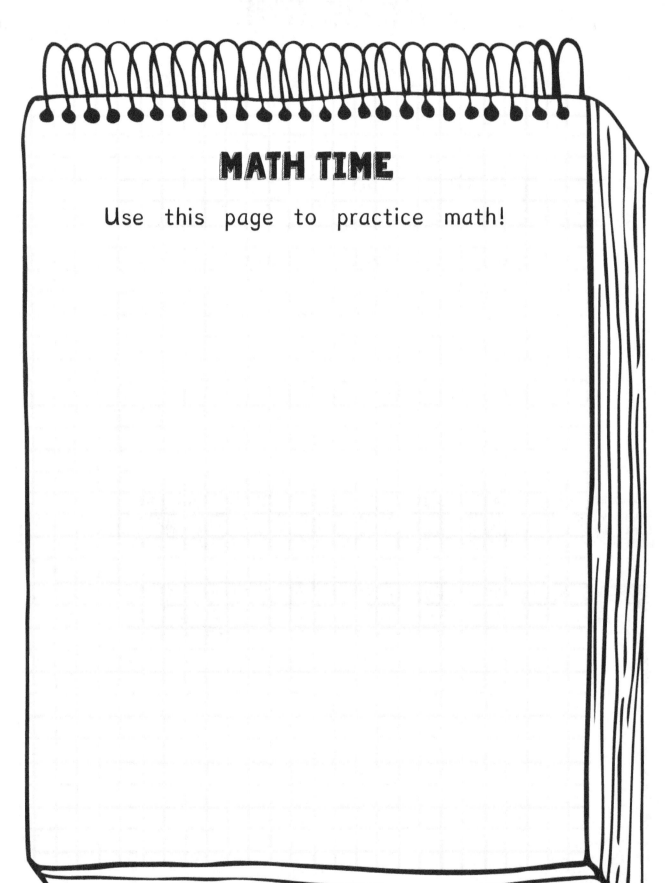

MATH TIME

Use this page to practice math!

Today I will read for

15   30   45   60

MINUTES

READING TIME

Write and draw about what you are reading.

ANIMAL FACTS
ROCK GREENLING

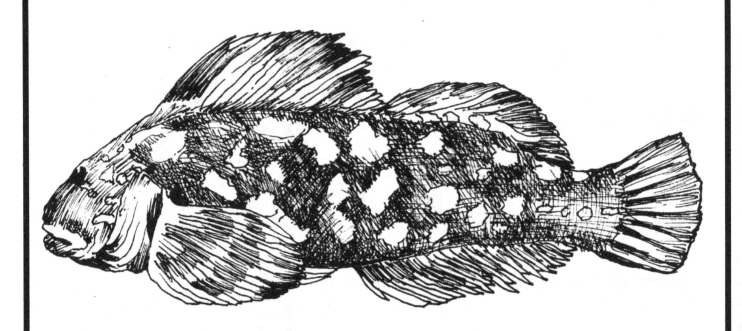

WRITE DOWN THREE FACTS ABOUT THIS ANIMAL:

1. _____

_____

2. _____

_____

3. _____

_____

RESEARCH & DISCOVERIES

USE LIBRARY BOOKS, ENCYCLOPEDIAS OR THE INTERNET TO LEARN MORE.

Color the parts of the world where this animal lives.

DRAW MY HOME	DRAW MY FOOD	DRAW MY ENEMIES

CREATIVE WRITING

Write a short story about these pictures.

_____

_____

_____

_____

_____

_____

_____

_____

_____

_____

_____

_____

_____

_____

_____

_____

_____

_____

_____

_____

CREATE A COMIC STRIP

CURSIVE WRITING PRACTICE

ANIMAL FACTS
ARCTIC ALLIGATORFISH

WRITE DOWN THREE FACTS ABOUT THIS ANIMAL:

1._____

_____

2._____

_____

3._____

_____

RESEARCH & DISCOVERIES

USE LIBRARY BOOKS, ENCYCLOPEDIAS OR THE INTERNET TO LEARN MORE.

Color the parts of the world where this animal lives.

DRAW MY HOME	DRAW MY FOOD	DRAW MY ENEMIES

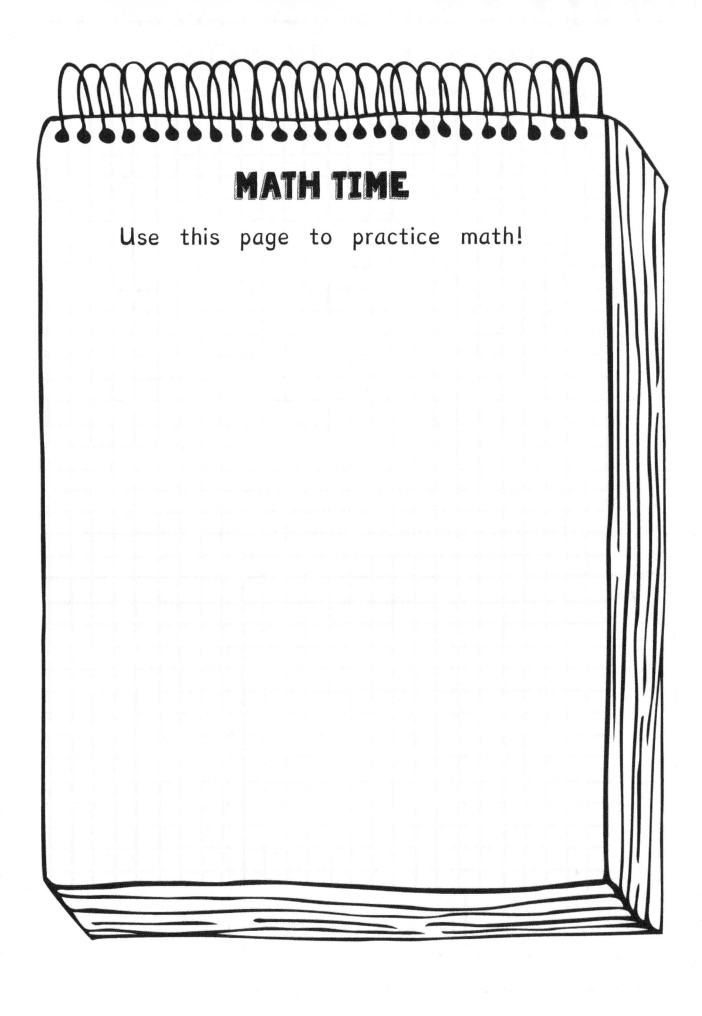

MATH TIME

Use this page to practice math!

LISTENING TIME

Listen to a podcast, audio book or inspiring music.

Draw and doodle below.

I am listening to: _____

CLIP ART

Use stickers, pictures from magazines, or print out pictures of ocean creatures from the internet and paste them on these pages.

DRAWING TIME

Copy a picture from any of your books.

ANIMAL FACTS
WALRUS

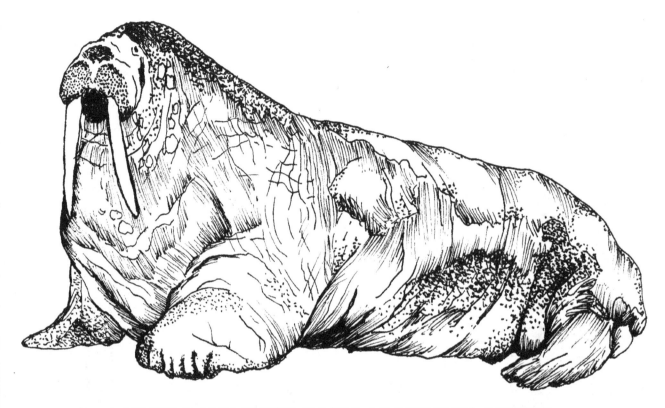

WRITE DOWN THREE FACTS ABOUT THIS ANIMAL:

1._____

_____

2._____

_____

3._____

_____

RESEARCH & DISCOVERIES

USE LIBRARY BOOKS, ENCYCLOPEDIAS OR THE INTERNET TO LEARN MORE.

Color the parts of the world where this animal lives.

DRAW MY HOME

DRAW MY FOOD

DRAW MY ENEMIES

Find creatures that are hidden in the picture

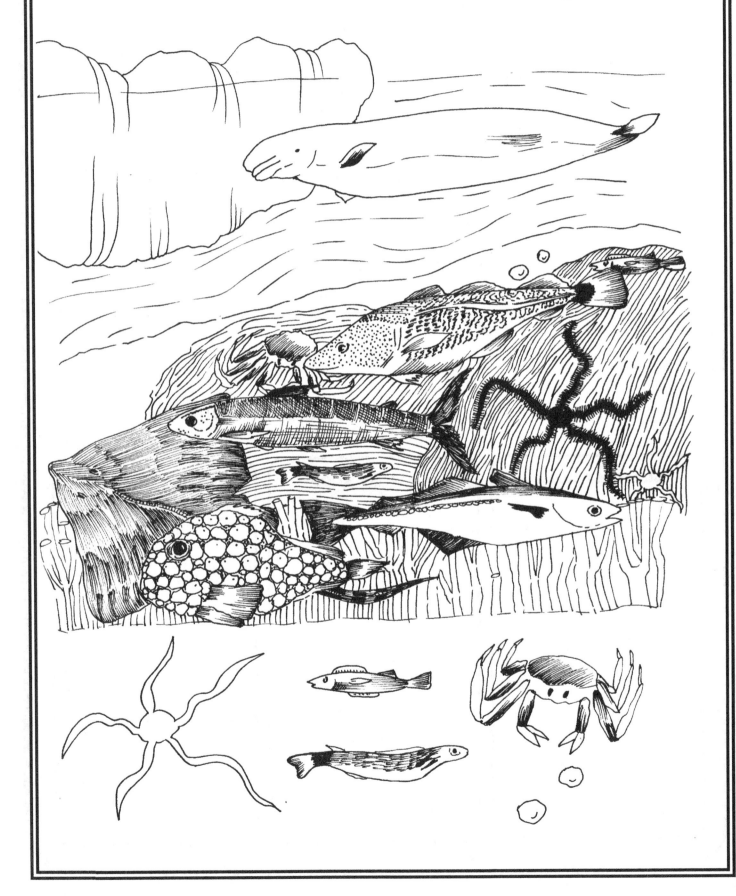

VOCABULARY BUILDING

Look in your Library Books

for **FOUR** words with more than **TEN** letters.

Write the words and their definitions below:

Bathypelagic zone of the Arctic ocean

Write 3 things about bathypelagic zone of the ocean

DRAWING TIME

Copy a picture from any of your books.

ANIMAL FACTS
LUMPSUCKER

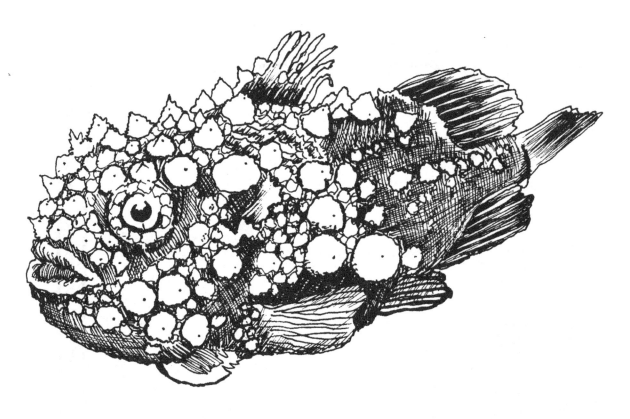

WRITE DOWN THREE FACTS ABOUT THIS ANIMAL:

1. _____

_____

2. _____

_____

3. _____

_____

RESEARCH & DISCOVERIES

USE LIBRARY BOOKS, ENCYCLOPEDIAS OR THE INTERNET TO LEARN MORE.

Color the parts of the world where this animal lives.

DRAW MY HOME	DRAW MY FOOD	DRAW MY ENEMIES

FAREWELL, TILL NEXT TIME

BY SHANNON AND ISABELLE SHEARN

Mommy and me visit the Sea.
Can't wait to dip my feet in the ocean,
a saltwater potion,
and leave footprints in the sand.
Hand-in-hand,
We walk along the shore,
gathering seashells to our heart's galore!
Gulls' wings flapping in the sky above,
the beach is a place we surely love!
Now as the sun sets atop the waves' rolling
tide,
we bid the sea farewell,
until next time!

REPLACE THE ADJECTIVES AND VERBS
TO MAKE A WHOLE NEW POEM!

Add artwork to the page.

Mommy and me _____ the Sea.
Can't wait to _____ my feet in the ocean,
a saltwater potion,
and leave footprints in the sand.
Hand-in-hand,
We _____ along the shore,
gathering seashells to our heart's galore!
Gulls' wings _____ in the sky above,
the beach is a place we surely love!
Now as the sun _____ atop the waves' rolling
tide,
we bid the sea farewell,
until next time!

MOVIE TIME

Watch a video about the ocean or ocean creatures!

TITLE:_____

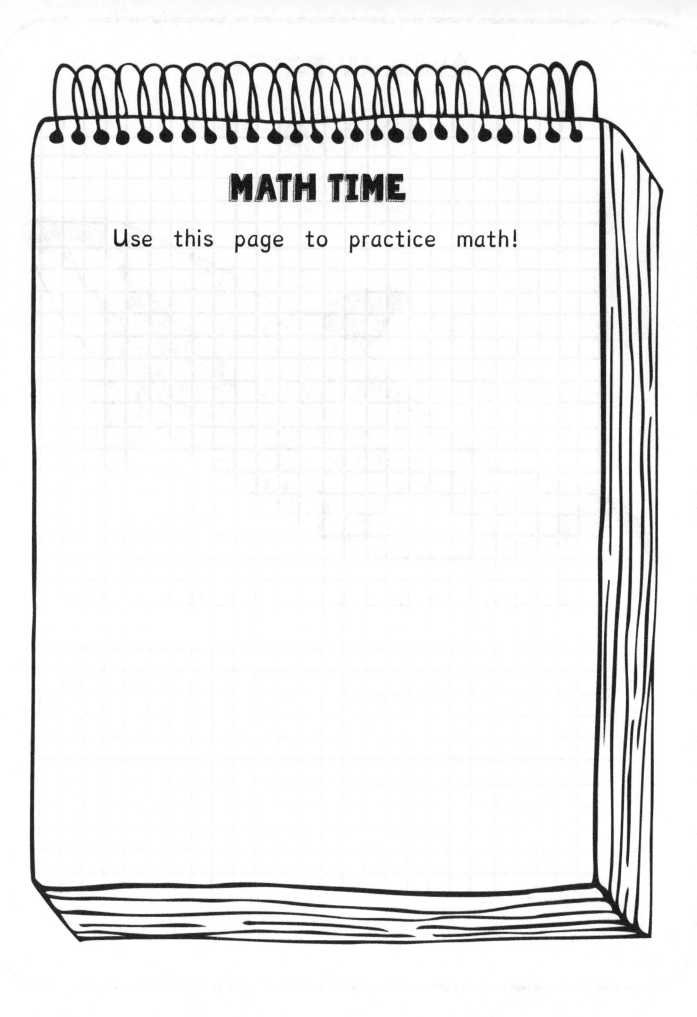

MATH TIME

Use this page to practice math!

ANIMAL FACTS
ORCA

WRITE DOWN THREE FACTS ABOUT THIS ANIMAL:

1._____

_____

2._____

_____

3._____

_____

RESEARCH & DISCOVERIES

USE LIBRARY BOOKS, ENCYCLOPEDIAS OR THE INTERNET TO LEARN MORE.

Color the parts of the world where this animal lives.

DRAW MY HOME	DRAW MY FOOD	DRAW MY ENEMIES

CREATE A COMIC STRIP

CURSIVE WRITING PRACTICE

ANIMAL FACTS
ARCTIC SKATE

WRITE DOWN THREE FACTS ABOUT THIS ANIMAL:

1._____

_____

2._____

_____

3._____

_____

RESEARCH & DISCOVERIES

USE LIBRARY BOOKS, ENCYCLOPEDIAS OR THE INTERNET TO LEARN MORE.

Color the parts of the world where this animal lives.

DRAW MY HOME	DRAW MY FOOD	DRAW MY ENEMIES

SNORKELING

BY AMBER HINKLE

The sun climbs beyond the edge,
golden strands through the water it wove,
Rising to warm the salty seabed.
Awaken slumbering coral cove.
Emerge, we've come to see
your scales shimmer,
as you wind through your seaweed grove.
Quiet and peaceful is your home,
In the great Pacific where we dove.

REPLACE THE ADJECTIVES AND VERBS
TO MAKE A WHOLE NEW POEM!

Add artwork to the page.

The sun _____ beyond the edge,
_____ strands through the water it _____,
_____ to warm the _____ seabed.
Awaken slumbering coral cove.
Emerge, we've come to see
your scales _____,
as you wind through your seaweed grove.
_____ and _____ is your home,
In the great Pacific where we dove.

CLIP ART

Use stickers, pictures from magazines, or print out pictures of ocean creatures from the internet and paste them on these pages.

LISTENING TIME

Listen to a podcast, audio book or inspiring music.

Draw and doodle below.

I am listening to: _____

MOVIE TIME

Watch a video about the ocean or ocean creatures!

TITLE:_____

RATING:

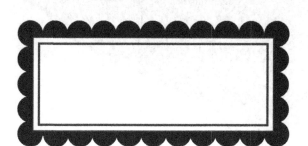

READING TIME

Write and draw about
what you are reading.

ANIMAL FACTS
GREENLAND SHARK

WRITE DOWN THREE FACTS ABOUT THIS ANIMAL:

1._____

_____

2._____

_____

3._____

_____

RESEARCH & DISCOVERIES

USE LIBRARY BOOKS, ENCYCLOPEDIAS OR THE INTERNET TO LEARN MORE.

Color the parts of the world where this animal lives.

DRAW MY HOME	DRAW MY FOOD	DRAW MY ENEMIES

SPELLING TIME

Pick a Letter _____

Look in your homeschooling books for

words that start with this letter.

Write ten spelling words.

1._____

2._____

3._____

4._____

5._____

6._____

7._____

8._____

9._____

10._____

DRAWING TIME

Copy a picture from any of your books.

ANIMAL FACTS
BELUGA WHALE

WRITE DOWN THREE FACTS ABOUT THIS ANIMAL:

1._____

_____

2._____

_____

3._____

_____

RESEARCH & DISCOVERIES

USE LIBRARY BOOKS, ENCYCLOPEDIAS OR THE INTERNET TO LEARN MORE.

Color the parts of the world where this animal lives.

DRAW MY HOME

DRAW MY FOOD

DRAW MY ENEMIES

CREATE A COMIC STRIP

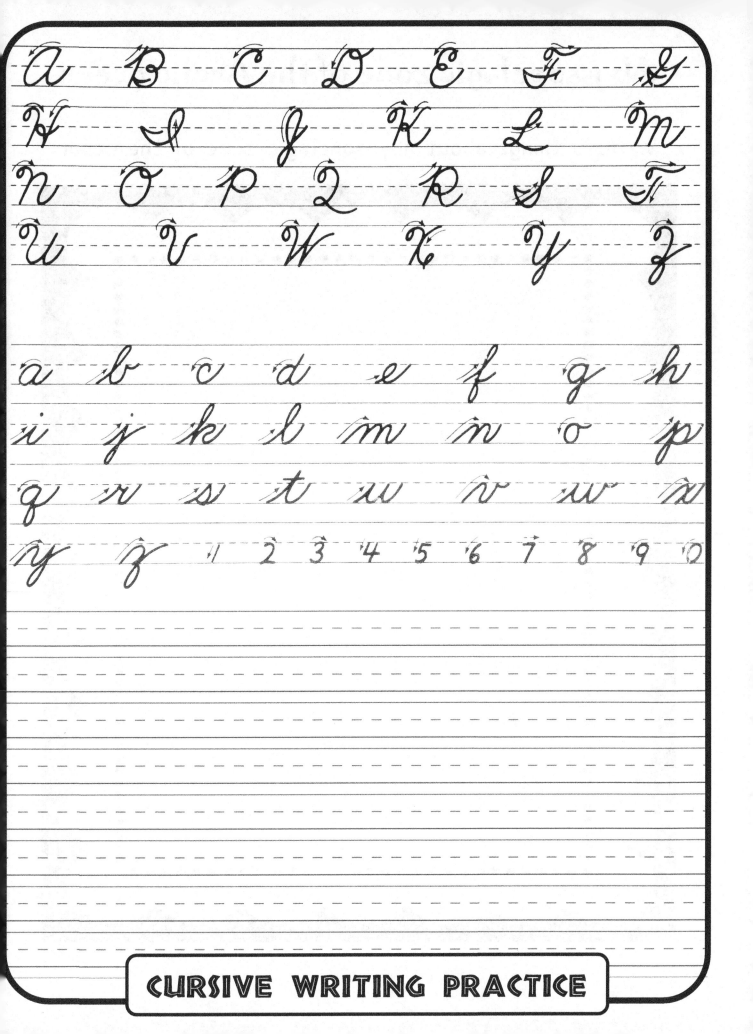

CURSIVE WRITING PRACTICE

Abyssopelagic zone of the Arctic ocean

Write 3 things about abyssopelagic zone of the ocean

Today I will
read for

15 30 45 60

MINUTES

READING
TIME

Write and draw about
what you are reading.

BRITTLE STARS

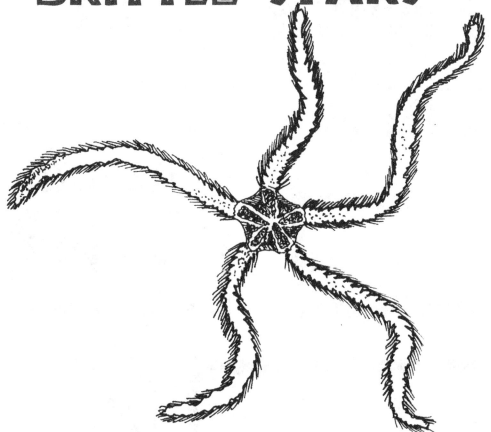

WRITE DOWN THREE FACTS ABOUT THIS ANIMAL:

1. _____

_____

2. _____

_____

3. _____

_____

RESEARCH & DISCOVERIES

USE LIBRARY BOOKS, ENCYCLOPEDIAS OR THE INTERNET TO LEARN MORE.

Color the parts of the world where this animal lives.

| DRAW MY HOME | DRAW MY FOOD | DRAW MY ENEMIES |

VOCABULARY BUILDING

Look in your Library Books

for **FOUR** words with more than **TEN** letters.

Write the words and their definitions below:

DRAWING TIME

Copy a picture from any of your books.

The Southern Ocean

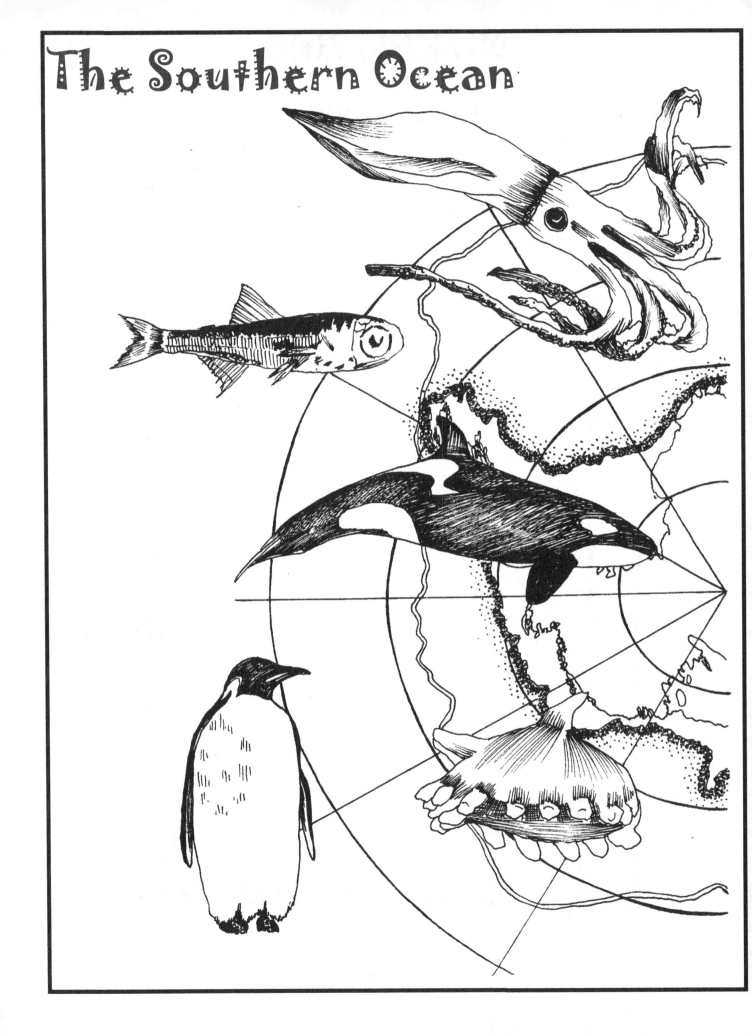

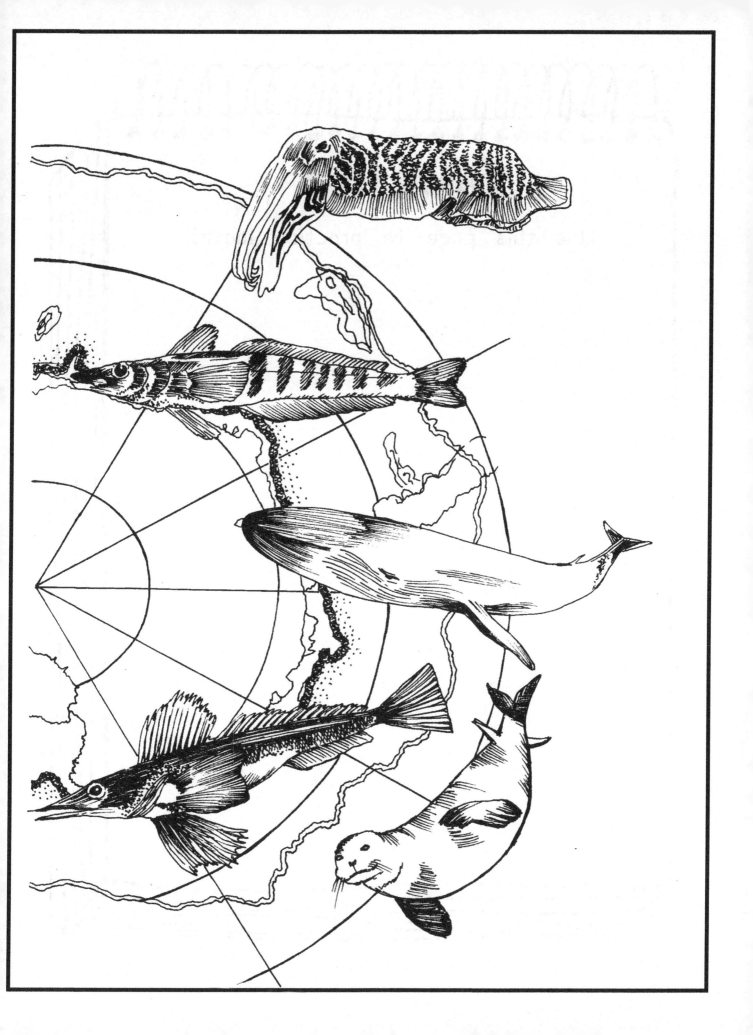

MATH TIME

Use this page to practice math!

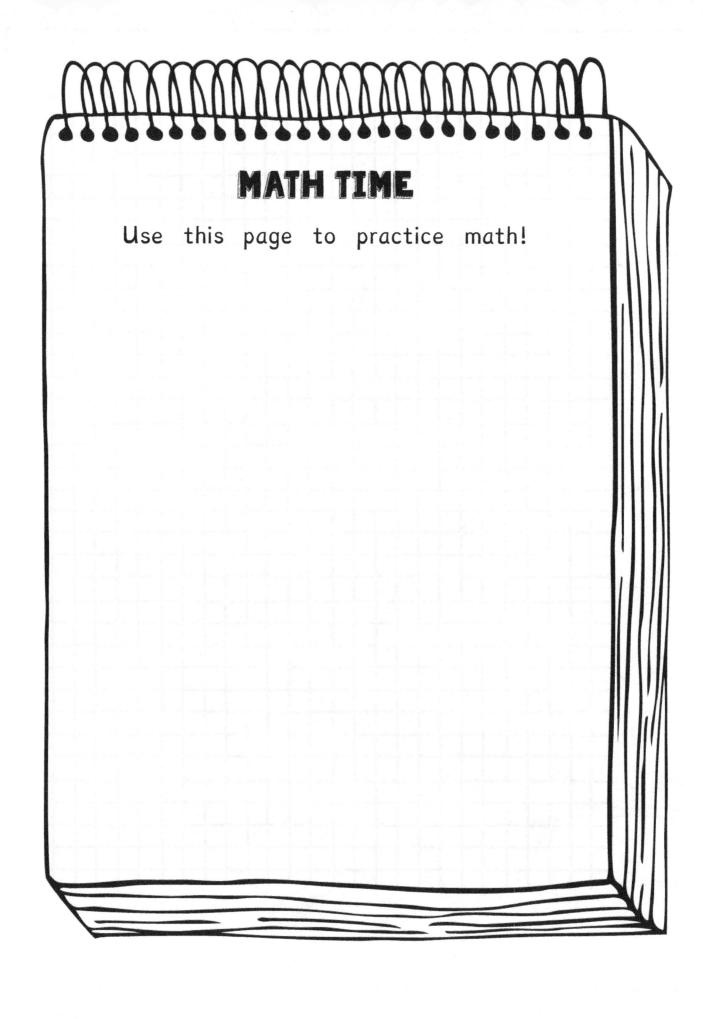

Epipelagic Zone of the Southern Ocean

Find creatures that are hidden in the picture

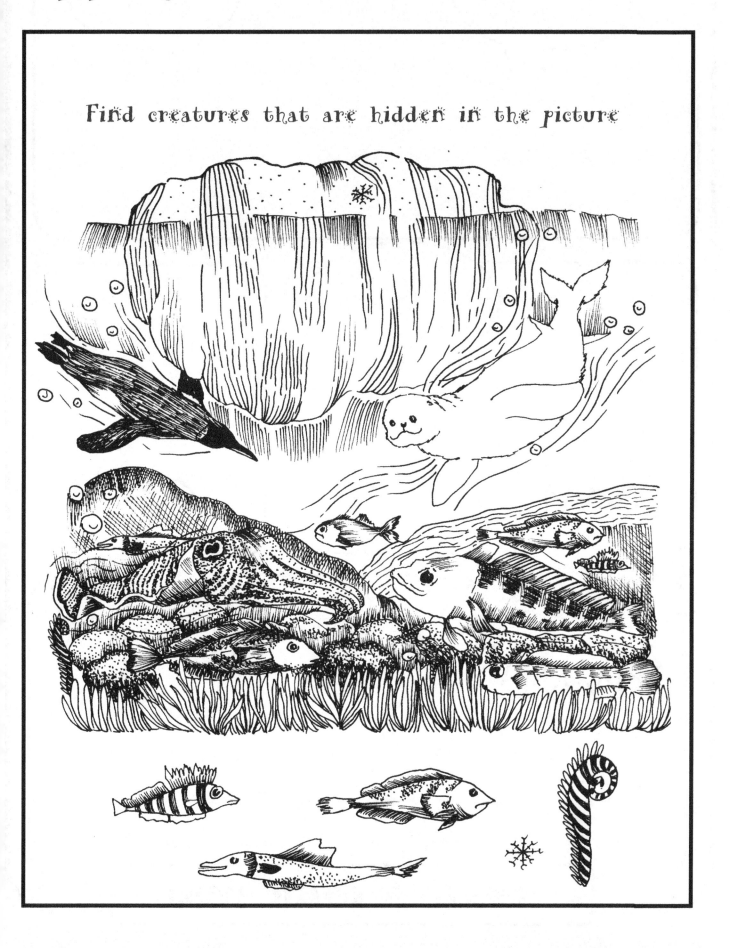

CREATE A COMIC STRIP

A B C D E F G
H I J K L M
N O P 2 R S T
U V W X Y Z

a b c d e f g h
i j k l m n o p
q r s t u v w x
y z 1 2 3 4 5 6 7 8 9 0

CURSIVE WRITING PRACTICE

ANIMAL FACTS
OCELLATED ICEFISH

WRITE DOWN THREE FACTS ABOUT THIS ANIMAL:

1._____

_____

2._____

_____

3._____

_____

RESEARCH & DISCOVERIES

USE LIBRARY BOOKS, ENCYCLOPEDIAS OR THE INTERNET TO LEARN MORE.

Color the parts of the world where this animal lives.

DRAW MY HOME

DRAW MY FOOD

DRAW MY ENEMIES

OCEAN LIFE

BY NORI HOBBS

Ocean so salty, fish so fast.
Every time we go, we have a blast.
Fish so friendly, ocean so blue.
Everything wants to say "hi" to you.
Coral so colorful, jellyfish clear.
The ocean I love, I hold it so near.
Jellyfish squishy, coral rough.
Leaving the ocean is always so tough.

REPLACE THE ADJECTIVES AND VERBS
TO MAKE A WHOLE NEW POEM!

Add artwork to the page.

Ocean so _____, fish so _____.
Every time we go, we have a _____.
Fish so _____, ocean so _____.
Everything wants to say "hi" to you.
Coral so _____, jellyfish _____.
The ocean I love, I hold it so near.
Jellyfish _____, coral _____.
_____ the ocean is always so _____.

MOVIE TIME

Watch a video about the ocean or ocean creatures!

TITLE:_____

RATING:

Draw Your Favorite Scenes:

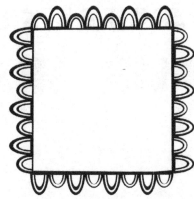

Today I will read for

15 30 45 60

MINUTES

READING TIME

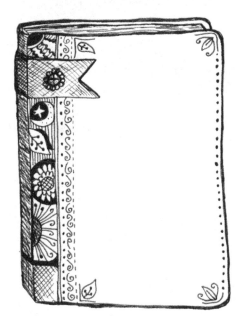

Write and draw about what you are reading.

ANIMAL FACTS
FUR SEAL

WRITE DOWN THREE FACTS ABOUT THIS ANIMAL:

1. _____

_____

2. _____

_____

3. _____

_____

RESEARCH & DISCOVERIES

USE LIBRARY BOOKS, ENCYCLOPEDIAS OR THE INTERNET TO LEARN MORE.

Color the parts of the world where this animal lives.

DRAW MY HOME	DRAW MY FOOD	DRAW MY ENEMIES

CLIP ART

Use stickers, pictures from magazines, or print out pictures of ocean creatures from the internet and paste them on these pages.

LISTENING TIME

Listen to a podcast, audio book or inspiring music.

Draw and doodle below.

I am listening to: _____

ANIMAL FACTS
EMPEROR PENGUIN

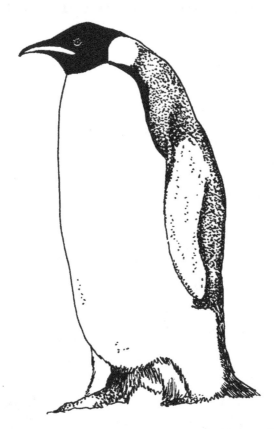

WRITE DOWN THREE FACTS ABOUT THIS ANIMAL:

1._____

_____

2._____

_____

3._____

_____

RESEARCH & DISCOVERIES

USE LIBRARY BOOKS, ENCYCLOPEDIAS OR THE INTERNET TO LEARN MORE.

Color the parts of the world where this animal lives.

DRAW MY HOME	DRAW MY FOOD	DRAW MY ENEMIES

PENGUIN LIFE

BY SHANNON AND ISABELLE SHEARN

A penguin here, a penguin there.
Little penguins everywhere!
Marching together one-by-one.
Waddling together to-&-from.
Black and white tuxedo feathers
– oh so sweet!
Standing tall on happy penguin feet.
Sliding over snow on plump penguin bellies.
Diving in the ocean for fish and jellies.
Huddling with one another back on land
to stay warm.
Giving gifts of pebbles to build a nest
with such charm!
The life of a penguin colony,
aquatic flightless swimmers with
quite the personality!

REPLACE THE ADJECTIVES AND VERBS
TO MAKE A WHOLE NEW POEM!

Add artwork to the page.

A penguin here, a penguin there.
_____ penguins everywhere!
_____ together one-by-one.
_____ together to-&-from.
_____ and _____ tuxedo feathers
- oh so sweet!
_____ tall on _____ penguin feet.
_____ over snow on _____ penguin bellies.
_____ in the ocean for fish and jellies.
_____ with one another back on land
to stay warm.
_____ gifts of pebbles to _____ a nest
with such charm!
The life of a penguin colony,
aquatic flightless swimmers with
quite the personality!

READING TIME

Write and draw about
what you are reading.

DRAWING TIME

Copy a picture from any of your books.

Mesopelagic zone of the Southern Ocean

Write **3** things about mesopelagic zone of the ocean

VOCABULARY BUILDING

Look in your Library Books

for **FOUR** words with more than **TEN** letters.

Write the words and their definitions below:

ANIMAL FACTS
BLUE WHALE

WRITE DOWN THREE FACTS ABOUT THIS ANIMAL:

1._____

_____

2._____

_____

3._____

_____

RESEARCH & DISCOVERIES

USE LIBRARY BOOKS, ENCYCLOPEDIAS OR THE INTERNET TO LEARN MORE.

Color the parts of the world where this animal lives.

DRAW MY HOME	DRAW MY FOOD	DRAW MY ENEMIES

CREATE A COMIC STRIP

A B C D E F G
H I J K L M
N O P Q R S T
U V W X Y Z

a b c d e f g h
i j k l m n o p
q r s t u v w x
y z 1 2 3 4 5 6 7 8 9 0

CURSIVE WRITING PRACTICE

ANIMAL FACTS
MACKEREL ICEFISH

WRITE DOWN THREE FACTS ABOUT THIS ANIMAL:

1._____
_____

2._____
_____

3._____
_____

RESEARCH & DISCOVERIES

USE LIBRARY BOOKS, ENCYCLOPEDIAS OR THE INTERNET TO LEARN MORE.

Color the parts of the world where this animal lives.

DRAW MY HOME	DRAW MY FOOD	DRAW MY ENEMIES

SPELLING TIME

Pick a Letter _____

Look in your homeschooling books for

words that start with this letter.

Write ten spelling words.

1._____

2._____

3._____

4._____

5._____

6._____

7._____

8._____

9._____

10._____

DRAWING TIME

Copy a picture from any of your books.

READING TIME

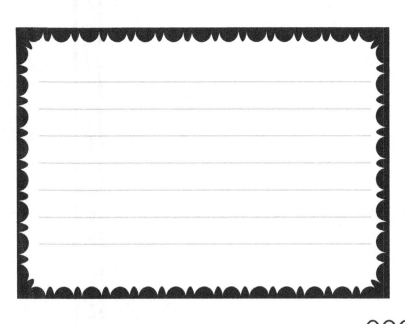

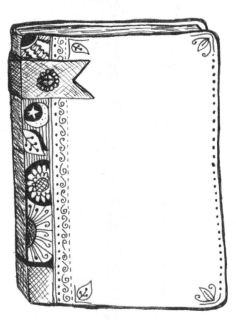

Write and draw about
what you are reading.

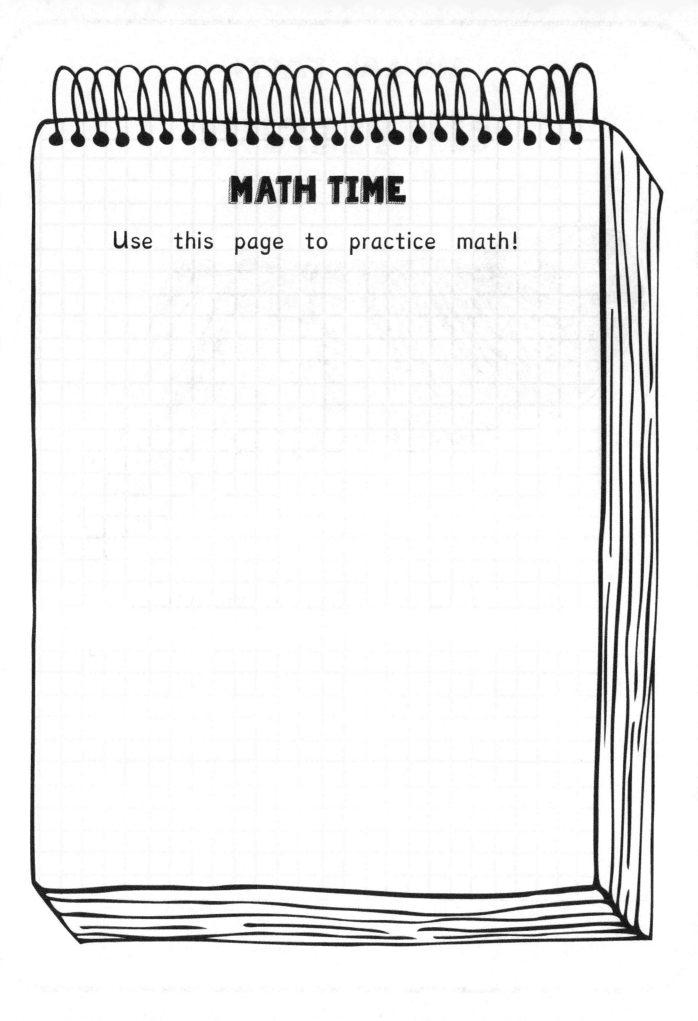

MATH TIME

Use this page to practice math!

ANIMAL FACTS
CUTTLEFISH

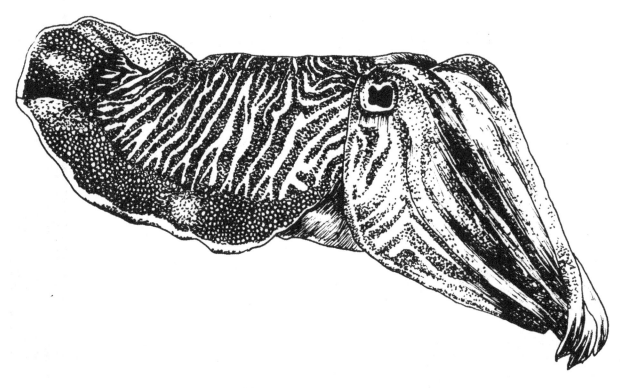

WRITE DOWN THREE FACTS ABOUT THIS ANIMAL:

1._____

_____

2._____

_____

3._____

_____

RESEARCH & DISCOVERIES

USE LIBRARY BOOKS, ENCYCLOPEDIAS OR THE INTERNET TO LEARN MORE.

Color the parts of the world where this animal lives.

DRAW MY HOME	DRAW MY FOOD	DRAW MY ENEMIES

MOVIE TIME

Watch a video about the ocean or ocean creatures!

TITLE:_____

RATING:

SPELLING TIME

Pick a Letter _____

Look in your homeschooling books for

words that start with this letter.

Write ten spelling words.

1._____

2._____

3._____

4._____

5._____

6._____

7._____

8._____

9._____

10._____

Bathypelagic zone of the Southern Ocean

Find creatures that are hidden in the picture

DRAWING TIME

Copy a picture from any of your books.

ANIMAL FACTS
Giant squid

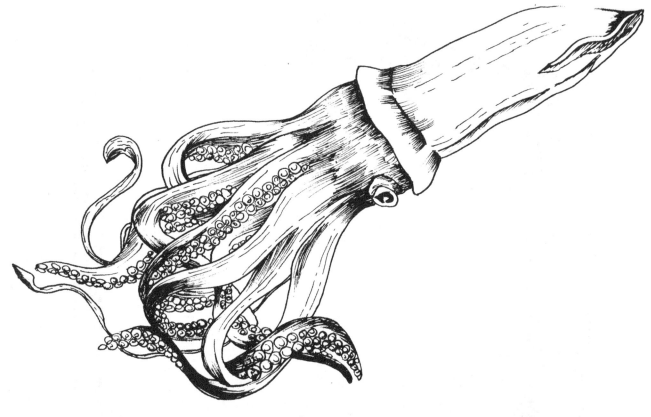

WRITE DOWN THREE FACTS ABOUT THIS ANIMAL:

1._____

_____

2._____

_____

3._____

_____

RESEARCH & DISCOVERIES

USE LIBRARY BOOKS, ENCYCLOPEDIAS OR THE INTERNET TO LEARN MORE.

Color the parts of the world where this animal lives.

DRAW MY HOME	DRAW MY FOOD	DRAW MY ENEMIES

Today I will read for

15 30 45 60

MINUTES

READING TIME

Write and draw about what you are reading.

LISTENING TIME

Listen to a podcast, audio book or inspiring music.

Draw and doodle below.

I am listening to: _____

ANIMAL FACTS

Sea pig

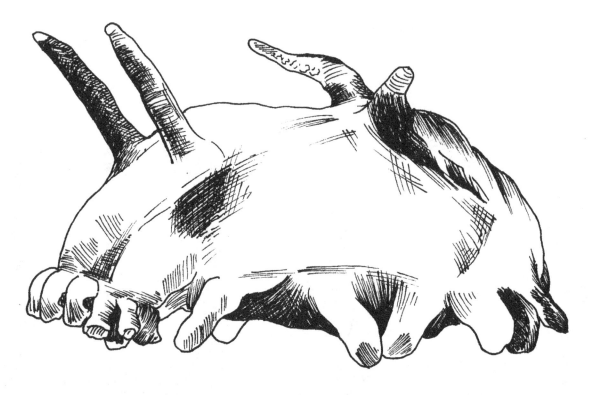

WRITE DOWN THREE FACTS ABOUT THIS ANIMAL:

1._____

_____

2._____

_____

3._____

_____

RESEARCH & DISCOVERIES

USE LIBRARY BOOKS, ENCYCLOPEDIAS OR THE INTERNET TO LEARN MORE.

Color the parts of the world where this animal lives.

DRAW MY HOME	DRAW MY FOOD	DRAW MY ENEMIES

MOVIE TIME

Watch a video about the ocean or ocean creatures!

TITLE:_____

RATING:

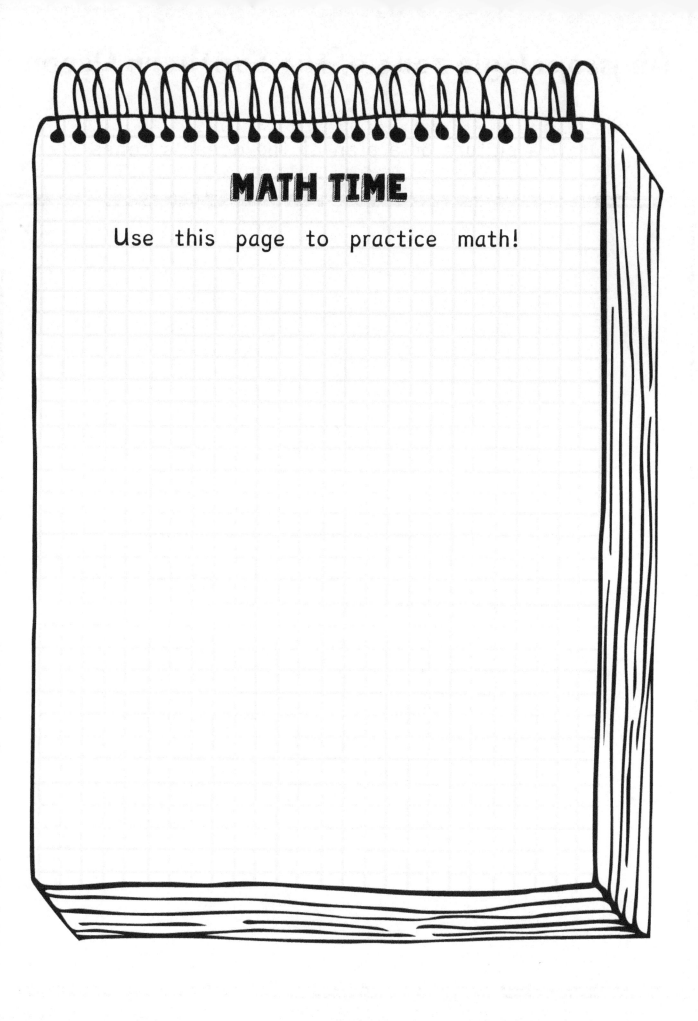

MATH TIME

Use this page to practice math!

Abyssopelagic zone of the Southern Ocean

Draw a picture or a plan of the ocean's zones

VOCABULARY BUILDING

Look in your Library Books

for **FOUR** words with more than **TEN** letters.

Write the words and their definitions below:

ANIMAL FACTS

Myctophid

WRITE DOWN THREE FACTS ABOUT THIS ANIMAL:

1._____

_____

2._____

_____

3._____

_____

RESEARCH & DISCOVERIES

USE LIBRARY BOOKS, ENCYCLOPEDIAS OR THE INTERNET TO LEARN MORE.

Color the parts of the world where this animal lives.

DRAW MY HOME

DRAW MY FOOD

DRAW MY ENEMIES

The Indian Ocean

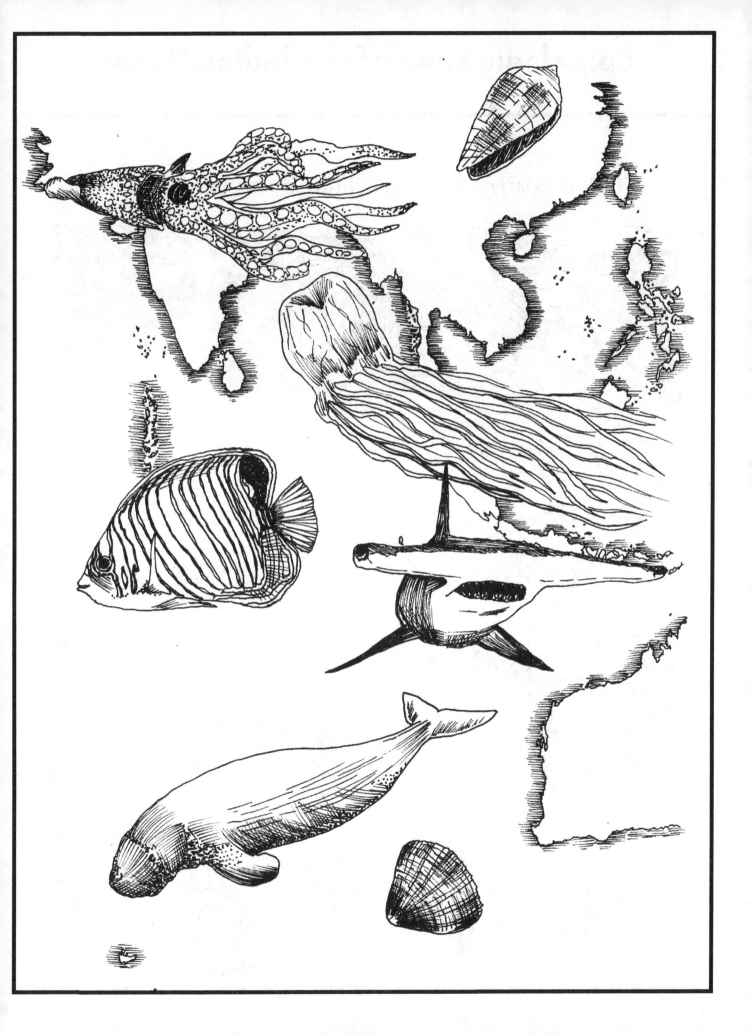

Epipelagic zone of the Indian Ocean

Find creatures that are hidden in the picture

COPYWORK

Copy a sentence from one of your library books.

TITLE: _____

Page#_____

_____

_____

_____

_____

_____

DRAWING TIME

Copy an illustration from one of your books.

THE INDIAN OCEAN

BY STEPHANIE JACOBS

The Indian Ocean,
vast and wide,
always in motion,
nothing to hide.
Dugong, turtles,
sharks, and whales,
swimming in circles,
splashing their tails.
Warm water is here,
the warmest around.
Unique species appear,
so much to be found.

REPLACE THE ADJECTIVES AND VERBS TO MAKE A WHOLE NEW POEM!

Add artwork to the page.

The Indian Ocean,
_____ and _____,
always in motion,
nothing to hide.
Dugong, turtles,
sharks, and whales,
_____ in circles,
_____ their tails.
_____ water is here,
the warmest around.
Unique species appear,
so much to be found.

ANIMAL FACTS
African penguin

WRITE DOWN THREE FACTS ABOUT THIS ANIMAL:

1._____

_____

2._____

_____

3._____

_____

RESEARCH & DISCOVERIES

USE LIBRARY BOOKS, ENCYCLOPEDIAS OR THE INTERNET TO LEARN MORE.

Color the parts of the world where this animal lives.

DRAW MY HOME	DRAW MY FOOD	DRAW MY ENEMIES

CREATE A COMIC STRIP

CURSIVE WRITING PRACTICE

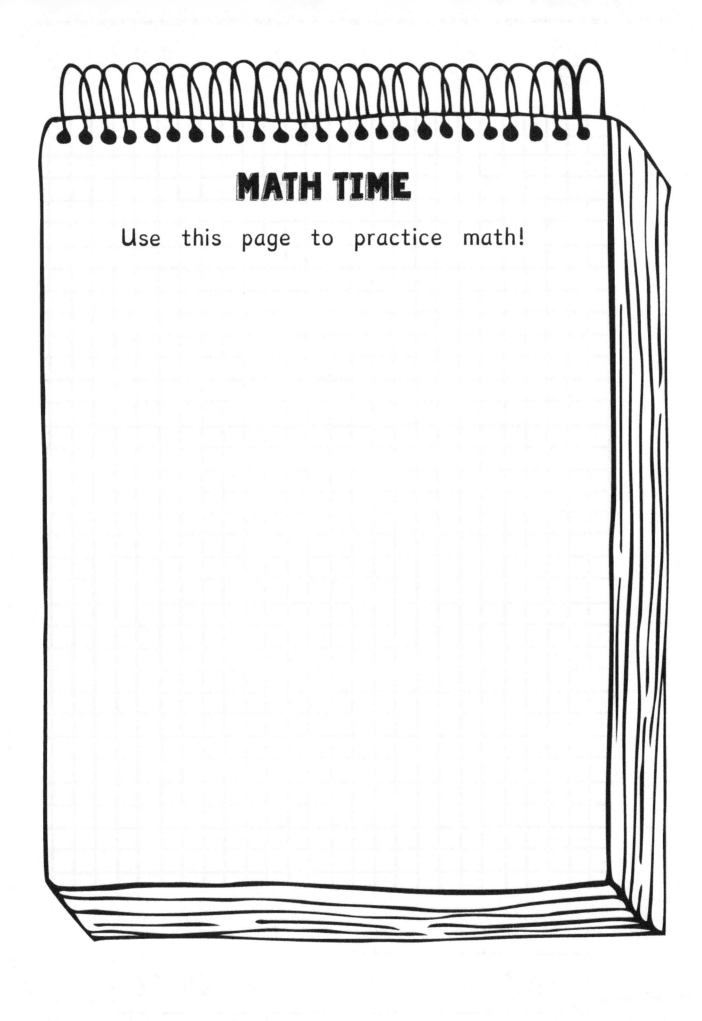

MATH TIME

Use this page to practice math!

MOVIE TIME

Watch a video about the ocean or ocean creatures!

TITLE:_____

RATING:

Draw Your Favorite Scenes:

ANIMAL FACTS

ANGELFISH

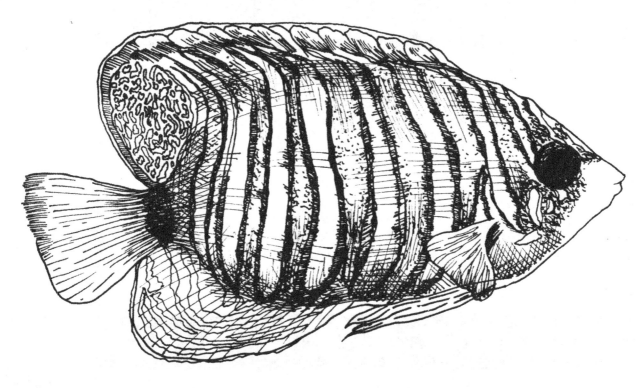

WRITE DOWN THREE FACTS ABOUT THIS ANIMAL:

1._____

_____

2._____

_____

3._____

_____

RESEARCH & DISCOVERIES

USE LIBRARY BOOKS, ENCYCLOPEDIAS OR THE INTERNET TO LEARN MORE.

Color the parts of the world where this animal lives.

DRAW MY HOME

DRAW MY FOOD

DRAW MY ENEMIES

Today I will
read for

15 30 45 60

MINUTES

READING TIME

Write and draw about
what you are reading.

DRAWING TIME

Copy a picture from any of your books.

ANIMAL FACTS
DUGONGS

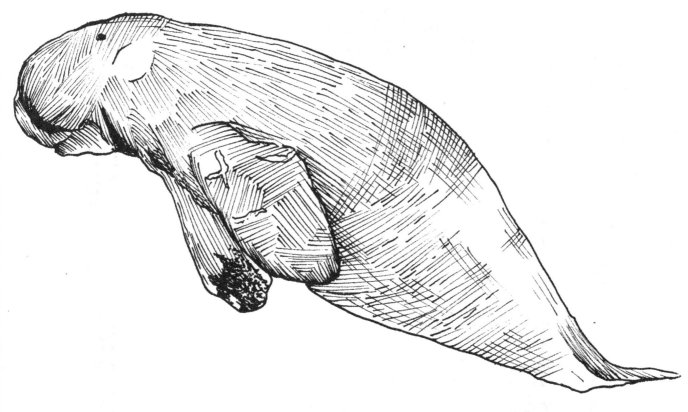

WRITE DOWN THREE FACTS ABOUT THIS ANIMAL:

1._____

_____

2._____

_____

3._____

_____

RESEARCH & DISCOVERIES

USE LIBRARY BOOKS, ENCYCLOPEDIAS OR THE INTERNET TO LEARN MORE.

Color the parts of the world where this animal lives.

DRAW MY HOME	DRAW MY FOOD	DRAW MY ENEMIES

OCEAN VIEW

BY ERICA AND TAGGART HORTON

Many, many seas.
Blue as can be.
Fluorescent coral patterns.
Magical in diversity.
Waves leisurely douse the shore.
Your vastness leaves much to explore.
The sun sets atop your tide.
In depths of darkness your treasures hide.
Your power so endless,
seamounts form an atoll.
You regulate the climate and nourish the soul.

REPLACE THE ADJECTIVES AND VERBS
TO MAKE A WHOLE NEW POEM!

Add artwork to the page.

Many, many seas.

_____ as can be.

Fluorescent coral patterns.

_____ in diversity.

Waves leisurely _____ the shore.

Your vastness leaves much to explore.

The sun _____ atop your tide.

In depths of _____ your treasures hide.

Your power so _____ ,

seamounts form an atoll.

You regulate the climate and nourish the soul.

CLIP ART

Use stickers, pictures from magazines, or print out pictures of ocean creatures from the internet and paste them on these pages.

LISTENING TIME

Listen to a podcast, audio book or inspiring music.

Draw and doodle below.

I am listening to: _____

ANIMAL FACTS
GREAT WHITE SHARK

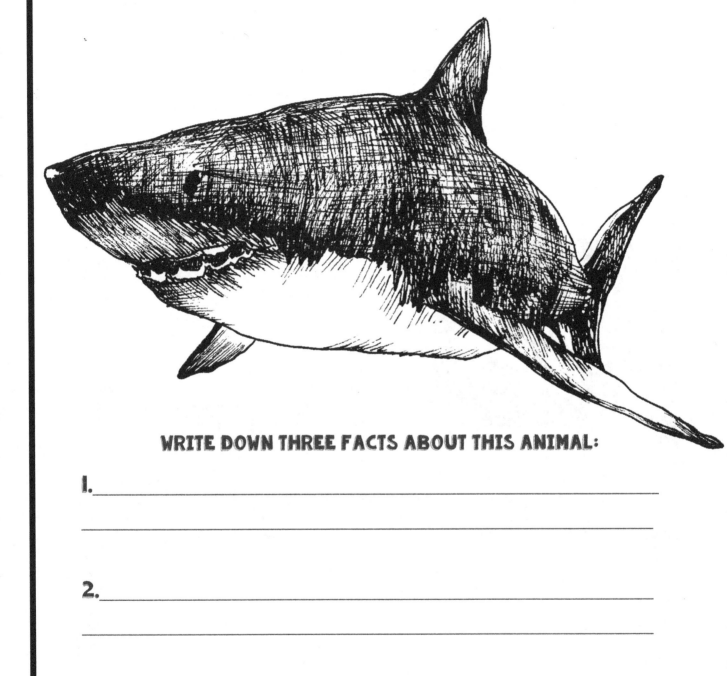

WRITE DOWN THREE FACTS ABOUT THIS ANIMAL:

1._____

_____

2._____

_____

3._____

_____

RESEARCH & DISCOVERIES

USE LIBRARY BOOKS, ENCYCLOPEDIAS OR THE INTERNET TO LEARN MORE.

Color the parts of the world where this animal lives.

DRAW MY HOME	DRAW MY FOOD	DRAW MY ENEMIES

GREAT WHITE

BY CHRISSY FOX

Grey on the top, white on the bottom.
300 rows of serrated triangular teeth.
Slow and stealthy get the prey.
Fast and swift time for dinner.
I don't mean harm to humans,
sometimes they just get in the way,
which causes everyone to have a bad day.
Many have made movies about me.
When you are here the music you know.
Here comes The Great White Shark!

REPLACE THE ADJECTIVES AND VERBS
TO MAKE A WHOLE NEW POEM!

Add artwork to the page.

_____ on the top, _____ on the bottom.
300 rows of serrated _____ teeth.
_____ and _____ get the prey.
_____ and _____ time for dinner.
I don't mean harm to humans,
sometimes they just get in the way,
which causes everyone to have a _____ day.
Many have _____ movies about me.
When you are here the music you know.
Here comes The Great White Shark!

CREATIVE WRITING

Write a short story about these pictures.

_____

_____

_____

_____

_____

_____

_____

_____

_____

_____

_____

_____

_____

_____

_____

_____

_____

_____

_____

_____

_____

ANIMAL FACTS
BOX JELLYFISH

WRITE DOWN THREE FACTS ABOUT THIS ANIMAL:

1._____

_____

2._____

_____

3._____

_____

RESEARCH & DISCOVERIES

USE LIBRARY BOOKS, ENCYCLOPEDIAS OR THE INTERNET TO LEARN MORE.

Color the parts of the world where this animal lives.

DRAW MY HOME	DRAW MY FOOD	DRAW MY ENEMIES

A JELLYFISH WISH

BY SHANNON AND ISABELLA SHEARN

Jellyfish-jelly, blob of the sea.
Swimming and bobbing,
Happy as can be!
Colors of the ocean everywhere,
Pink, yellow, orange, blue,
purple and even clear!
Oh, luminescent jellyfish,
glowing in the dark,
make a wish!

REPLACE THE ADJECTIVES AND VERBS
TO MAKE A WHOLE NEW POEM!

Add artwork to the page.

Jellyfish-jelly, blob of the sea.
_____ and _____,
_____ as can be!
Colors of the ocean everywhere,
Pink, yellow, orange, blue,
purple and even clear!
Oh, luminescent jellyfish,
_____ in the dark,
make a wish!

MOVIE TIME

Watch a video about the ocean or ocean creatures!

TITLE:_____

RATING:

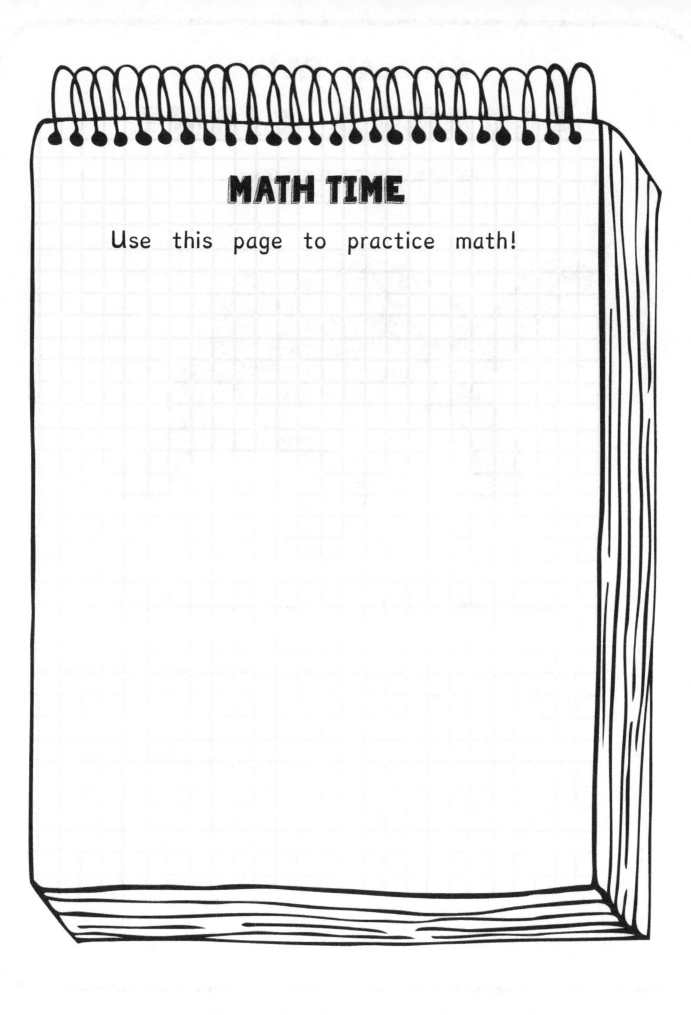

MATH TIME

Use this page to practice math!

ANIMAL FACTS
ALDABRA GIANT TORTOISE

WRITE DOWN THREE FACTS ABOUT THIS ANIMAL:

1._____

_____

2._____

_____

3._____

_____

RESEARCH & DISCOVERIES

USE LIBRARY BOOKS, ENCYCLOPEDIAS OR THE INTERNET TO LEARN MORE.

Color the parts of the world where this animal lives.

DRAW MY HOME	DRAW MY FOOD	DRAW MY ENEMIES

CREATE A COMIC STRIP

A B C D E F G
H I J K L M
N O P Q R S T
U V W X Y Z

a b c d e f g h
i j k l m n o p
q r s t u v w x
y z 1 2 3 4 5 6 7 8 9 0

CURSIVE WRITING PRACTICE

Mesopelagic zone of the Indian Ocean

Practice drawing ocean creatures

VOCABULARY BUILDING

Look in your Library Books

for **FOUR** words with more than **TEN** letters.

Write the words and their definitions below:

ANIMAL FACTS

GREAT HAMMERHEAD

WRITE DOWN THREE FACTS ABOUT THIS ANIMAL:

1._____

_____

2._____

_____

3._____

_____

RESEARCH & DISCOVERIES

USE LIBRARY BOOKS, ENCYCLOPEDIAS OR THE INTERNET TO LEARN MORE.

Color the parts of the world where this animal lives.

DRAW MY HOME	DRAW MY FOOD	DRAW MY ENEMIES

WHAT AM I?

BY DUSTIN AND DALTON PARKER

If I was a fish,
I wouldn't be a dish.
I'm sharp as a spear,
and have no fear.
If I swim by,
I may go a fly.
I'm lost at sea,
but home and free.
I hide in the deep,
but the shallows I reap.
What am I?

(A Great White Shark)

REPLACE THE ADJECTIVES AND VERBS
TO MAKE A WHOLE NEW POEM!

Add artwork to the page.

If I was a fish,
I wouldn't be a dish.
I'm _____ as a spear,
and have no fear.
If I _____ by,
I may go a fly.
I'm _____ at sea,
but home and free.
I _____ in the deep,
but the shallows I reap.
What am I?

(A Great White Shark)

Today I will
read for

15 30 45 60

MINUTES

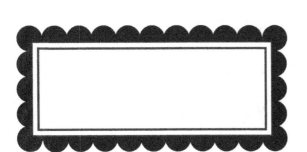

READING TIME

Write and draw about
what you are reading.

DRAWING TIME

Copy a picture from any of your books.

ANIMAL FACTS
SWORDFISH

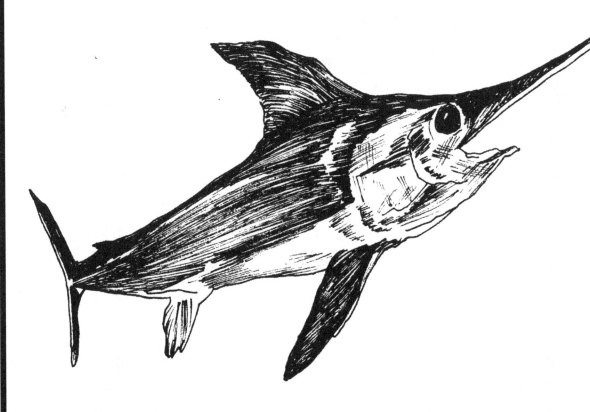

WRITE DOWN THREE FACTS ABOUT THIS ANIMAL:

1._____

_____

2._____

_____

3._____

_____

RESEARCH & DISCOVERIES

USE LIBRARY BOOKS, ENCYCLOPEDIAS OR THE INTERNET TO LEARN MORE.

Color the parts of the world where this animal lives.

DRAW MY HOME	DRAW MY FOOD	DRAW MY ENEMIES

Bathypelagic zone of the Indian Ocean

Find creatures that are hidden in the picture

COPYWORK

Copy a sentence from one of your library books.

TITLE: _____

Page#_____

_____

_____

_____

_____

_____

DRAWING TIME

Copy an illustration from one of your books.

ANIMAL FACTS
FLOWERVASE JEWEL SQUID

WRITE DOWN THREE FACTS ABOUT THIS ANIMAL:

1._____

_____

2._____

_____

3._____

_____

RESEARCH & DISCOVERIES

USE LIBRARY BOOKS, ENCYCLOPEDIAS OR THE INTERNET TO LEARN MORE.

Color the parts of the world where this animal lives.

DRAW MY HOME	DRAW MY FOOD	DRAW MY ENEMIES

CLOWNFISH

BY NORI HOBBS

Colors orange and white,
even violet, or black.
Like all clownfish it is highly
prized by aquarists all over the world.
Often found in small groups
Western Pacific Ocean is where
they call home.
New baby fish are called fry.
Food for sharks in saltwater.
Slimy and scaley habitat coral and seabeds.

REPLACE THE ADJECTIVES AND VERBS
TO MAKE A WHOLE NEW POEM!

Add artwork to the page.

Colors orange and white,
even violet, or black.
Like all clownfish it is highly
_____ by aquarists all over the world.
Often _____ in _____ groups
Western Pacific Ocean is where
they call home.
_____ baby fish are called fry.
Food for sharks in saltwater.
_____ and _____ habitat coral and seabeds.

CREATE A COMIC STRIP

A B C D E F G

H I J K L M

N O P Q R S T

U V W X Y Z

a b c d e f g h

i j k l m n o p

q r s t u v w x

y z 1 2 3 4 5 6 7 8 9 0

CURSIVE WRITING PRACTICE

Abyssopelagic zone of the Indian Ocean

Practice drawing ocean creatures

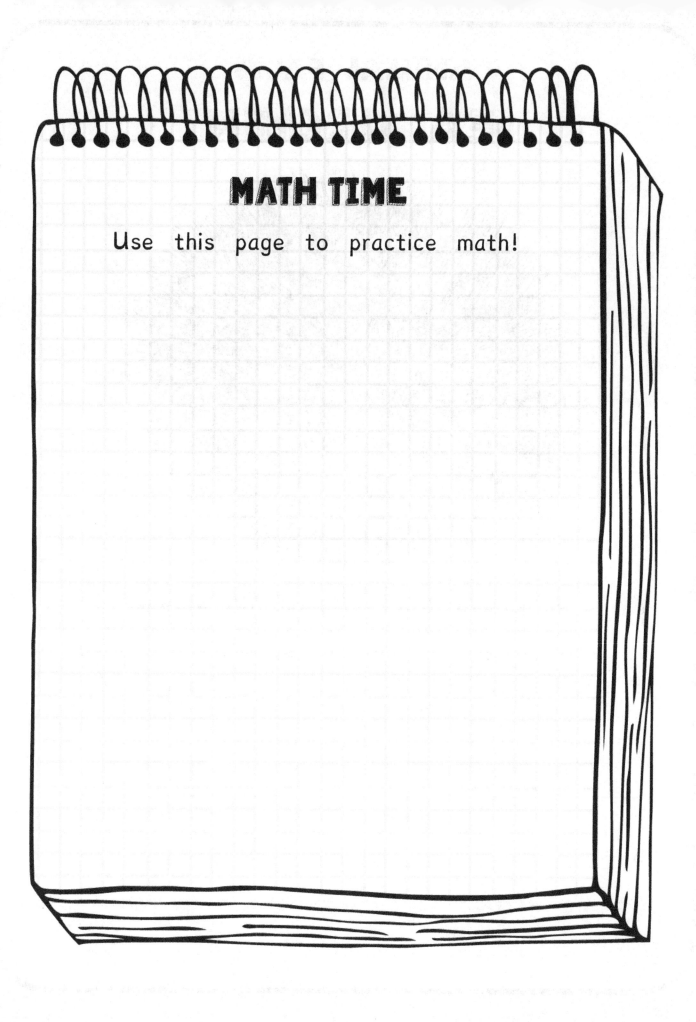

MATH TIME

Use this page to practice math!

ANIMAL FACTS
SEA URCHIN

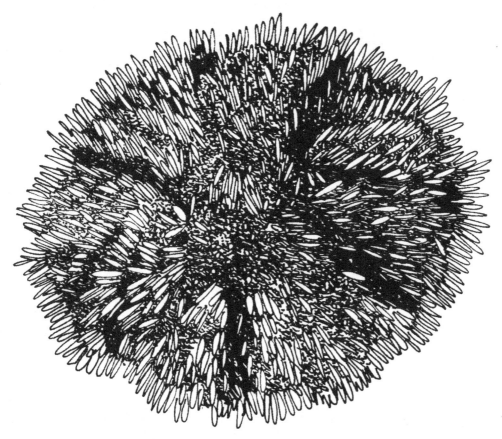

WRITE DOWN THREE FACTS ABOUT THIS ANIMAL:

1._____

_____

2._____

_____

3._____

_____

RESEARCH & DISCOVERIES

USE LIBRARY BOOKS, ENCYCLOPEDIAS OR THE INTERNET TO LEARN MORE.

Color the parts of the world where this animal lives.

DRAW MY HOME	DRAW MY FOOD	DRAW MY ENEMIES

The Atlantic Ocean

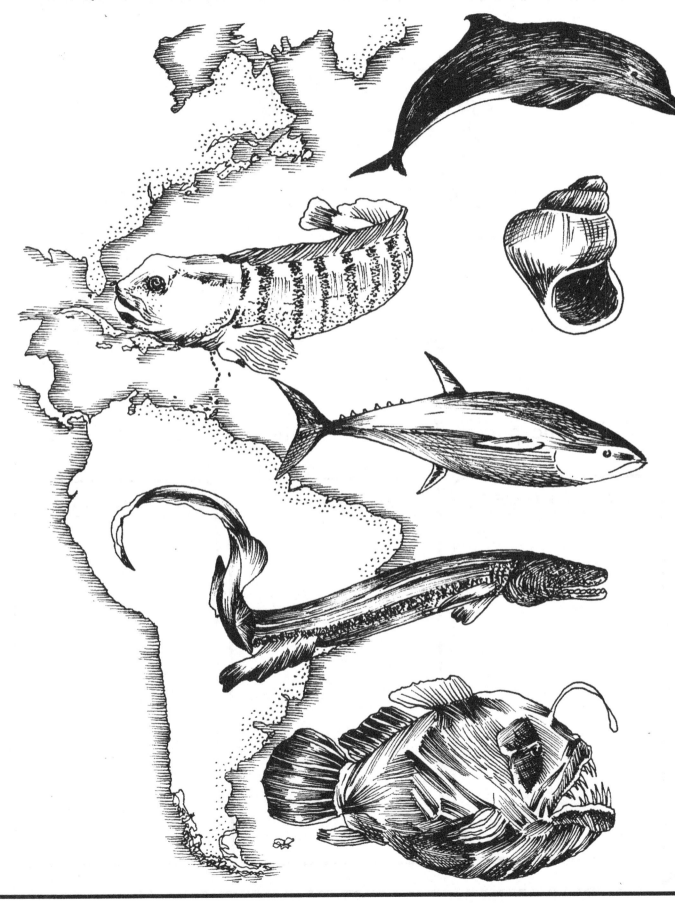

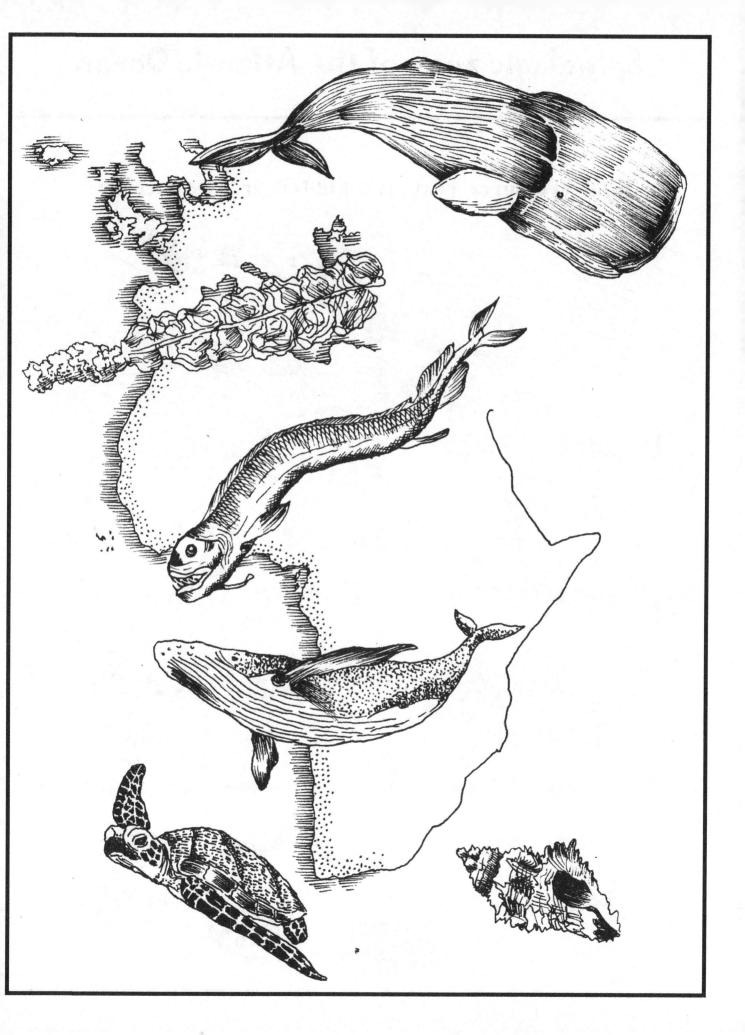

Epipelagic zone of the Atlantic Ocean

Find creatures that are hidden in the picture

MOVIE TIME

Watch a video about the ocean or ocean creatures!

TITLE:_____

RATING:

ATLANTIC OCEAN HEART

BY SHANNON DESMOND-SHEARN

We live not far from the sea.
The Atlantic Ocean calls to me,
as I remember fond childhood memories.
Let's visit the coastline!
A trip to the beach is the grandest of times!
Wake up early and Mom would pack a cooler
while Dad would pack the car.
We wouldn't have to travel very far.
Just over an hour's drive, take your pick:
Silver Sands, Hammonasset,
Ocean Beach, Misquamicut, Rocky Neck
and so many more!
How lucky we were to spend our summer
days at the seashore!
Soaking up the sun, toes in the sand, building "drip"
sandcastles, collecting shells and spotting a crab!
Feeding the seagulls, spending hours riding the waves,
playing on the boardwalk, climbing the rocks
and window shopping at the little seaside shoppes!
The salty air calms my soul and
beautiful sunsets had me from the start!
The Atlantic Ocean will always
hold a piece of my heart!

REPLACE THE ADJECTIVES AND VERBS
TO MAKE A WHOLE NEW POEM!

Add artwork to the page.

We _____ not far from the sea.
The Atlantic Ocean calls to me,
as I remember fond childhood memories.
Let's _____ the coastline!
A trip to the beach is the grandest of times!
Wake up early and Mom would _____ a cooler
while Dad would pack the car.
We wouldn't have to _____ very far.
Just over an hour's drive, take your pick:
Silver Sands, Hammonasset,
Ocean Beach, Misquamicut, Rocky Neck
and so many more!
How lucky we were to spend our summer
days at the seashore!
Soaking up the sun, toes in the sand, building "drip"
sandcastles, _____ shells and _____ a crab!
_____ the seagulls, spending hours _____ the waves,
playing on the boardwalk, _____ the rocks
and window shopping at the little seaside shoppes!
The _____ air calms my soul and
_____ sunsets had me from the start!
The Atlantic Ocean will always
_____ a piece of my heart!

READING TIME

Write and draw about
what you are reading.

LISTENING TIME

Listen to a podcast, audio book or inspiring music.

Draw and doodle below.

I am listening to: _____

ANIMAL FACTS

ATLANTIC BOTTLENOSE DOLPHINS

WRITE DOWN THREE FACTS ABOUT THIS ANIMAL:

1._____

_____

2._____

_____

3._____

_____

RESEARCH & DISCOVERIES

USE LIBRARY BOOKS, ENCYCLOPEDIAS OR THE INTERNET TO LEARN MORE.

Color the parts of the world where this animal lives.

DRAW MY HOME

DRAW MY FOOD

DRAW MY ENEMIES

THE OCEAN

BY CARMEN KLOPPERS

I close my eyes and smell the air.
It's saltiness is everywhere.
The dolphin glides with grace you see.
It dives and jumps so free, so free.
The whale and the shark at play,
while the octopus slips away.
The seal dips and dives down deep.
I feel the sand beneath my feet.
The ocean lies before my eyes,
its ever changing, moving tides.
You have many secrets kept inside.
I wish I could come take a ride.

REPLACE THE ADJECTIVES AND VERBS
TO MAKE A WHOLE NEW POEM!

Add artwork to the page.

I _____ my eyes and _____ the air.
It's saltiness is everywhere.
The dolphin _____ with grace you see.
It _____ and _____ so free, so free.
The whale and the shark at play,
while the octopus _____ away.
The seal _____ and _____ down deep.
I feel the _____ beneath my feet.
The ocean lies before my eyes,
its ever changing, _____ tides.
You have many secrets kept inside.
I wish I could come take a ride.

CLIP ART

Use stickers, pictures from magazines, or print out pictures of ocean creatures from the internet and paste them on these pages.

DRAWING TIME

Copy a picture from any of your books.

ANIMAL FACTS
GREEN SEA TURTLE

WRITE DOWN THREE FACTS ABOUT THIS ANIMAL:

1._____

_____

2._____

_____

3._____

_____

RESEARCH & DISCOVERIES

USE LIBRARY BOOKS, ENCYCLOPEDIAS OR THE INTERNET TO LEARN MORE.

Color the parts of the world where this animal lives.

DRAW MY HOME	DRAW MY FOOD	DRAW MY ENEMIES

HATCHLINGS

BY AMBER HINKLE

Dig, dig, dig your way out.
"There is the sun and ocean", we shout.
"Brothers and sisters, we must reach the sea."
"Move as fast as you can. Follow me!"

Our shells are soft, but our fins are strong.
Into the waves we paddle along.
Into the ocean we know nothing about.
But our instincts are strong,
so we have no reason to doubt.

Sea turtles we are.
We feel the urge to travel far.
But, for some, this shore has a catch.
They will return to leave a new nest to hatch.

REPLACE THE ADJECTIVES AND VERBS
TO MAKE A WHOLE NEW POEM!

Add artwork to the page.

Dig, dig, dig your way out.
"There is the sun and ocean", we _____.
"Brothers and sisters, we must reach the sea."
"Move as _____ as you can. Follow me!"

Our shells are _____, but our fins are _____.
Into the waves we _____ along.
Into the ocean we know nothing about.
But our instincts are _____,
so we have no reason to doubt.

Sea turtles we are.
We feel the urge to _____ far.
But, for some, this shore has a catch.
They will _____ to leave a new nest to _____.

CREATE A COMIC STRIP

A B C D E F G
H I J K L M
N O P Q R S T
U V W X Y Z

a b c d e f g h
i j k l m n o p
q r s t u v w x
y z 1 2 3 4 5 6 7 8 9 0

CURSIVE WRITING PRACTICE

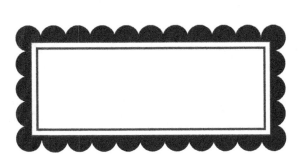

READING TIME

Write and draw about
what you are reading.

SPELLING TIME

Pick a Letter _____

Look in your homeschooling books for

words that start with this letter.

Write ten spelling words.

1._____

2._____

3._____

4._____

5._____

6._____

7._____

8._____

9._____

10._____

ANIMAL FACTS
HUMPBACK WHALE

WRITE DOWN THREE FACTS ABOUT THIS ANIMAL:

1. _____

_____

2. _____

_____

3. _____

_____

RESEARCH & DISCOVERIES

USE LIBRARY BOOKS, ENCYCLOPEDIAS OR THE INTERNET TO LEARN MORE.

Color the parts of the world where this animal lives.

DRAW MY HOME	DRAW MY FOOD	DRAW MY ENEMIES

Mesopelagic zone of the Atlantic Ocean

Practice drawing ocean creatures

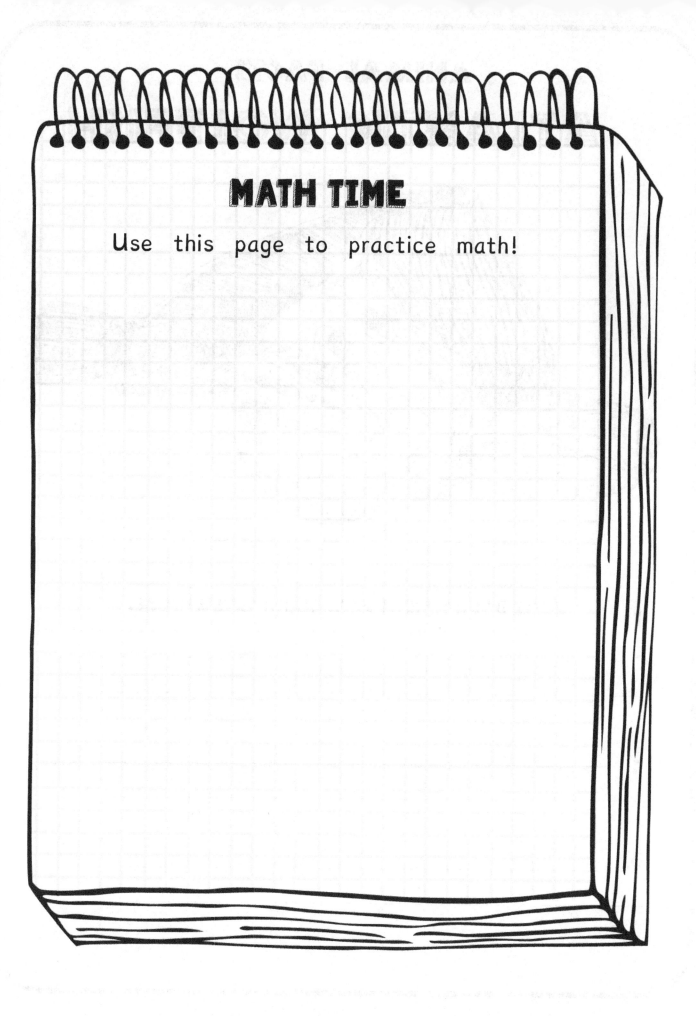

MATH TIME

Use this page to practice math!

ANIMAL FACTS
ATLANTIC WOLFFISH

WRITE DOWN THREE FACTS ABOUT THIS ANIMAL:

1._____

_____

2._____

_____

3._____

_____

RESEARCH & DISCOVERIES
USE LIBRARY BOOKS, ENCYCLOPEDIAS OR THE INTERNET TO LEARN MORE.

Color the parts of the world where this animal lives.

DRAW MY HOME	DRAW MY FOOD	DRAW MY ENEMIES

CAPTIVATING COQUINAS

BY RHIANNON JONES

Thy beauty shineth like stars in the sky.
Your grace is too much to handle for one's eye.
No one can see the creature you hide inside.
Your shell is seen during low tide.
Into the sand you dive so deep.
Oh, how your shell is so unique!

REPLACE THE ADJECTIVES AND VERBS
TO MAKE A WHOLE NEW POEM!

Add artwork to the page.

Thy beauty _____ like stars in the sky.
Your grace is too much to handle for one's eye.
No one can _____ the creature you hide inside.
Your shell is _____ during low tide.
Into the sand you _____ so deep.
Oh, how your shell is so _____ !

DRAWING TIME

Copy a picture from any of your books.

COPYWORK

Copy a sentence from one of your library books.

TITLE: _____

Page#_____

_____

_____

_____

_____

_____

DRAWING TIME

Copy an illustration from one of your books.

ANIMAL FACTS

SIPHONOPHORAE

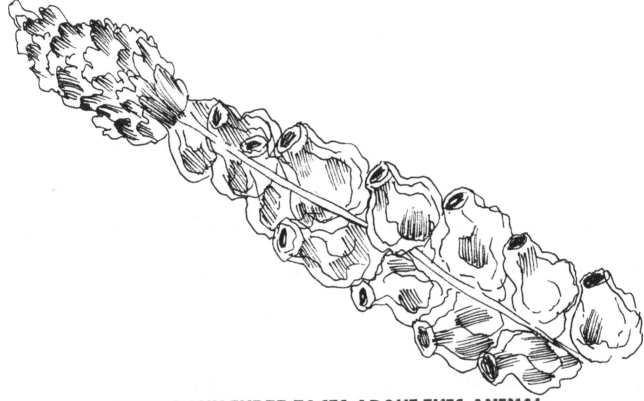

WRITE DOWN THREE FACTS ABOUT THIS ANIMAL:

1._____

_____

2._____

_____

3._____

_____

RESEARCH & DISCOVERIES

USE LIBRARY BOOKS, ENCYCLOPEDIAS OR THE INTERNET TO LEARN MORE.

Color the parts of the world where this animal lives.

DRAW MY HOME	DRAW MY FOOD	DRAW MY ENEMIES

MOVIE TIME

Watch a video about the ocean or ocean creatures!

TITLE:_____

RATING:

SPELLING TIME

Pick a Letter _____

Look in your homeschooling books for

words that start with this letter.

Write ten spelling words.

1._____

2._____

3._____

4._____

5._____

6._____

7._____

8._____

9._____

10._____

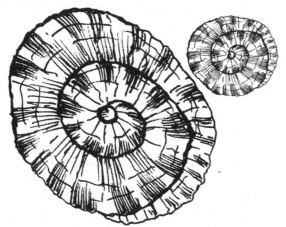

ANIMAL FACTS
ATLANTIC BLUEFIN TUNA

WRITE DOWN THREE FACTS ABOUT THIS ANIMAL:

1._____

_____

2._____

_____

3._____

_____

RESEARCH & DISCOVERIES

USE LIBRARY BOOKS, ENCYCLOPEDIAS OR THE INTERNET TO LEARN MORE.

Color the parts of the world where this animal lives.

DRAW MY HOME	DRAW MY FOOD	DRAW MY ENEMIES

CREATE A COMIC STRIP

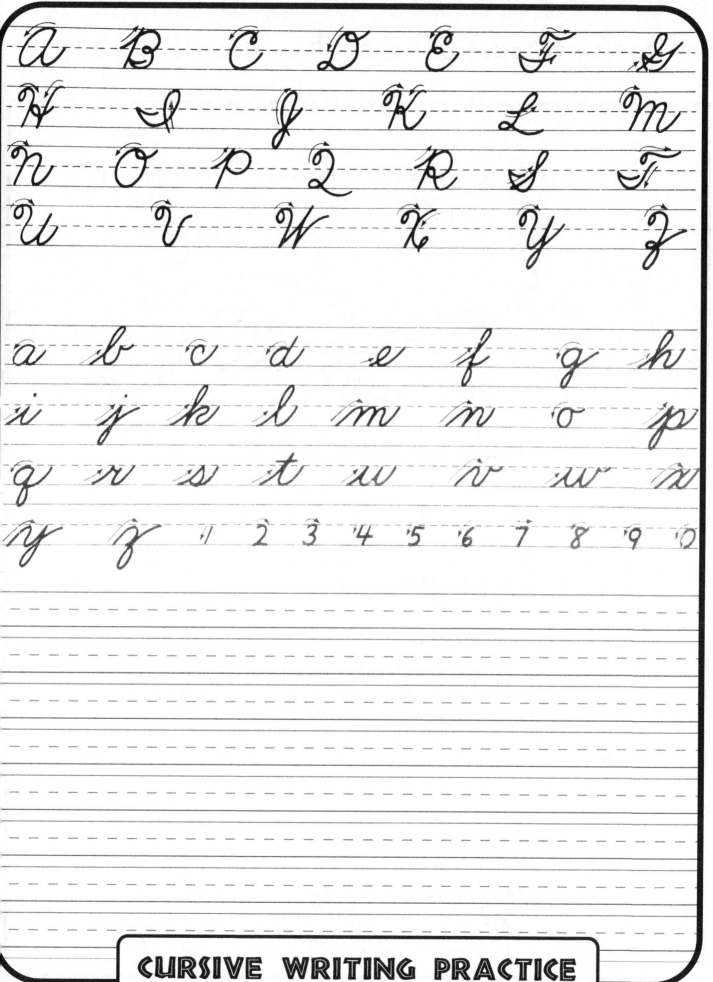

CURSIVE WRITING PRACTICE

Bathypelagic zone of the Atlantic Ocean

Find creatures that are hidden in the picture

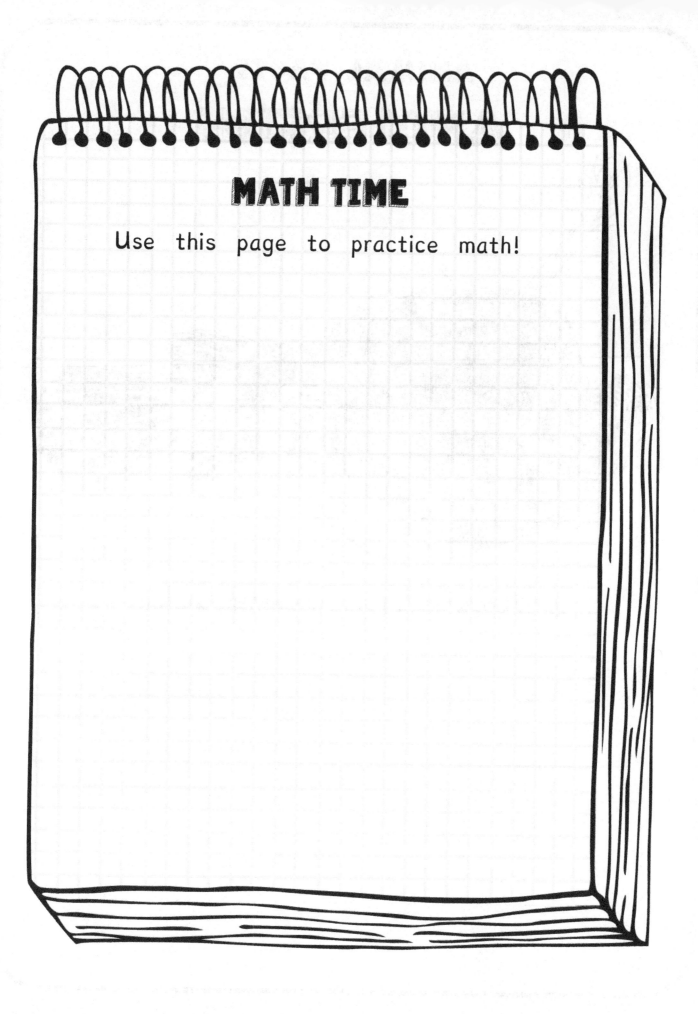

MATH TIME

Use this page to practice math!

ANIMAL FACTS
ANGLERFISH

WRITE DOWN THREE FACTS ABOUT THIS ANIMAL:

1._____

_____

2._____

_____

3._____

_____

RESEARCH & DISCOVERIES

USE LIBRARY BOOKS, ENCYCLOPEDIAS OR THE INTERNET TO LEARN MORE.

Color the parts of the world where this animal lives.

DRAW MY HOME	DRAW MY FOOD	DRAW MY ENEMIES

SEASIDE SUMMERS

BY MICHELLE WALKER HARRISON

As my feet touched the sand,
my child reaches for my hand.
When the sun lights our face,
we take in its warm embrace.
Overwhelmed by the deep,
Atlantic Ocean's boundary keep.
We see ocean waves,
roll and hit upon the caves.

The tide rolls out, can nothing hide?
even turtles must abide.
The water glistens, and shore recedes,
revealing seashell blooms like weeds.
Sea oats and beach flowers cover the dunes,
salty winds sing a relaxing tune.
Seagulls and boys enjoy the sea,
at sunset more time to play is their plea.
Time stands still, and evening sets,
moonlight krill iridesce;
My children's memories of the beach,
will be the lessons that we teach.

REPLACE THE ADJECTIVES AND VERBS
TO MAKE A WHOLE NEW POEM!

Add artwork to the page.

As my feet _____ the sand,
my child _____ for my hand.
When the sun _____ our face,
we take in its _____ embrace.
Overwhelmed by the deep,
Atlantic Ocean's boundary keep.
We _____ ocean waves,
_____ and hit upon the caves.

The tide _____ out, can nothing hide?
even turtles must abide.
The water _____, and shore recedes,
revealing seashell blooms like weeds.
Sea oats and beach flowers cover the dunes,
_____ winds sing a _____ tune.
Seagulls and boys _____ the sea,
at sunset more time to _____ is their plea.
Time _____ still, and evening sets,
moonlight krill iridesce;
My children's memories of the beach,
will be the lessons that we _____.

LISTENING TIME

Listen to a podcast, audio book or inspiring music.

Draw and doodle below.

I am listening to: _____

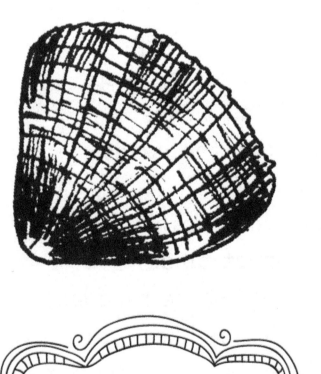

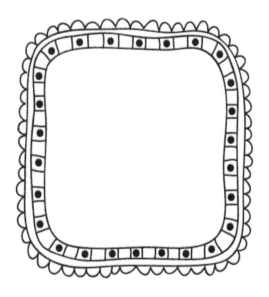

DRAWING TIME

Copy a picture from any of your books.

ANIMAL FACTS
FRILLED SHARK

WRITE DOWN THREE FACTS ABOUT THIS ANIMAL:

1._____

_____

2._____

_____

3._____

_____

RESEARCH & DISCOVERIES

USE LIBRARY BOOKS, ENCYCLOPEDIAS OR THE INTERNET TO LEARN MORE.

Color the parts of the world where this animal lives.

DRAW MY HOME

DRAW MY FOOD

DRAW MY ENEMIES

Today I will
read for

15 30 45 60

MINUTES

READING
TIME

Write and draw about
what you are reading.

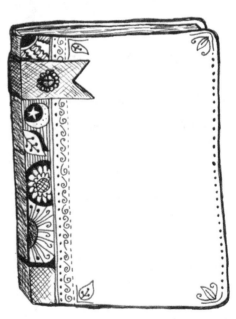

DRAWING TIME

Copy a picture from any of your books.

ANIMAL FACTS
SPERM WHALE

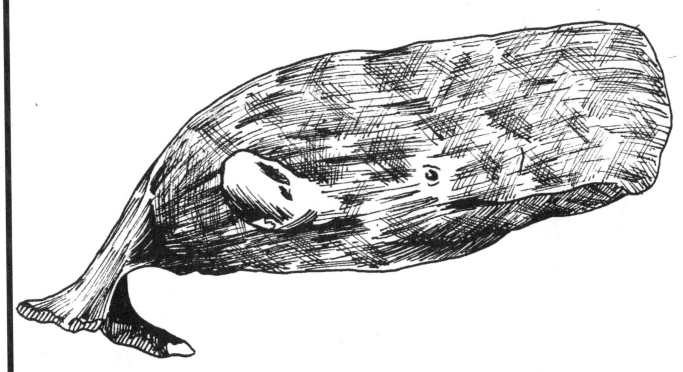

WRITE DOWN THREE FACTS ABOUT THIS ANIMAL:

1._____

_____

2._____

_____

3._____

_____

RESEARCH & DISCOVERIES

USE LIBRARY BOOKS, ENCYCLOPEDIAS OR THE INTERNET TO LEARN MORE.

Color the parts of the world where this animal lives.

DRAW MY HOME	DRAW MY FOOD	DRAW MY ENEMIES

A HERMIT CRAB'S HOME

BY SHANNON AND ISABELLE SHEARN

A hermit crab's home is a shell by the sea.
Oh, how lucky you must be,
little hermit crab looking at me!
Snug as a bug in your shell of choice,
but eyes on the sky when you hear the gull's
noise!
Wouldn't want to be a hermit without a shell,
for that may not go so swell!
Tide pools & salt marshes serve you well,
as you search for food all day.
Oh, the stories you'd tell!
A hermit crab's home is a shell by the sea,
growing, upgrading, scurrying around me!

REPLACE THE ADJECTIVES AND VERBS
TO MAKE A WHOLE NEW POEM!

Add artwork to the page.

A hermit crab's home is a shell by the sea.
Oh, how _____ you must be,
_____ hermit crab looking at me!
Snug as a bug in your shell of choice,
but eyes on the sky when you _____ the gull's
noise!
Wouldn't want to be a hermit without a shell,
for that may not go so swell!
Tide pools & salt marshes serve you well,
as you _____ for food all day.
Oh, the stories you'd tell!
A hermit crab's home is a shell by the sea,
growing, upgrading, _____ around me!

Abyssopelagic zone of the Atlantic Ocean

Practice drawing ocean creatures

SPELLING TIME

Pick a Letter _____

Look in your homeschooling books for

words that start with this letter.

Write ten spelling words.

1. _____

2. _____

3. _____

4. _____

5. _____

6. _____

7. _____

8. _____

9. _____

10. _____

Today I will read for

15 30 45 60

MINUTES

READING TIME

Write and draw about what you are reading.

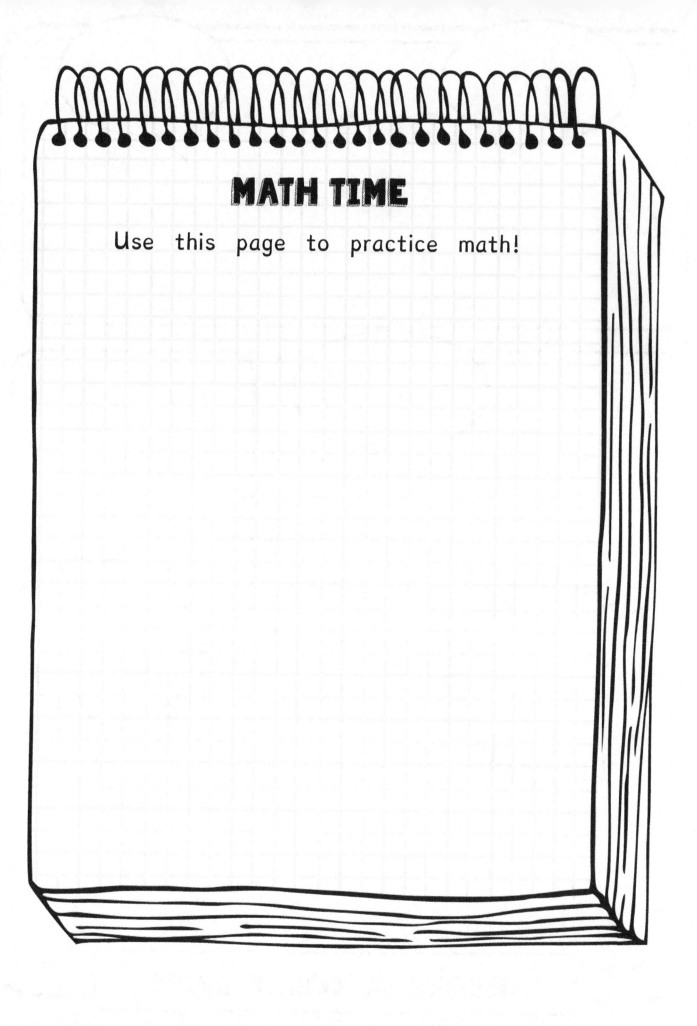

MATH TIME

Use this page to practice math!

CREATE A COMIC STRIP

A B C D E F G

H I J K L M

N O P Q R S T

U V W X Y Z

a b c d e f g h

i j k l m n o p

q r s t u v w x

y z 1 2 3 4 5 6 7 8 9 0

CURSIVE WRITING PRACTICE

The Pacific Ocean

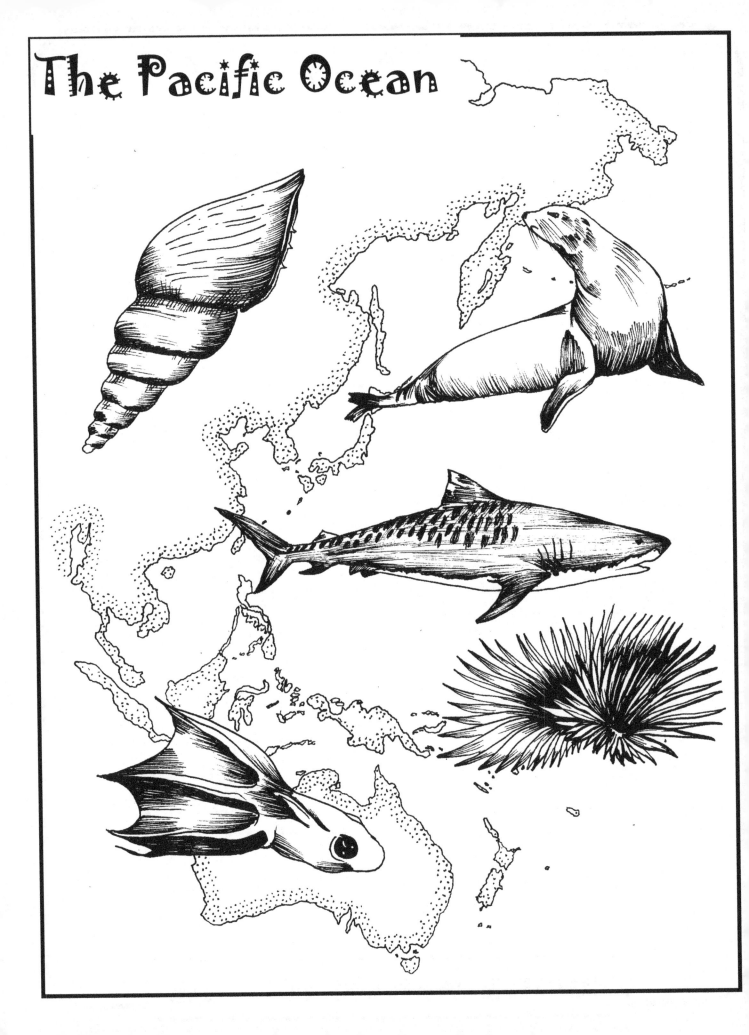

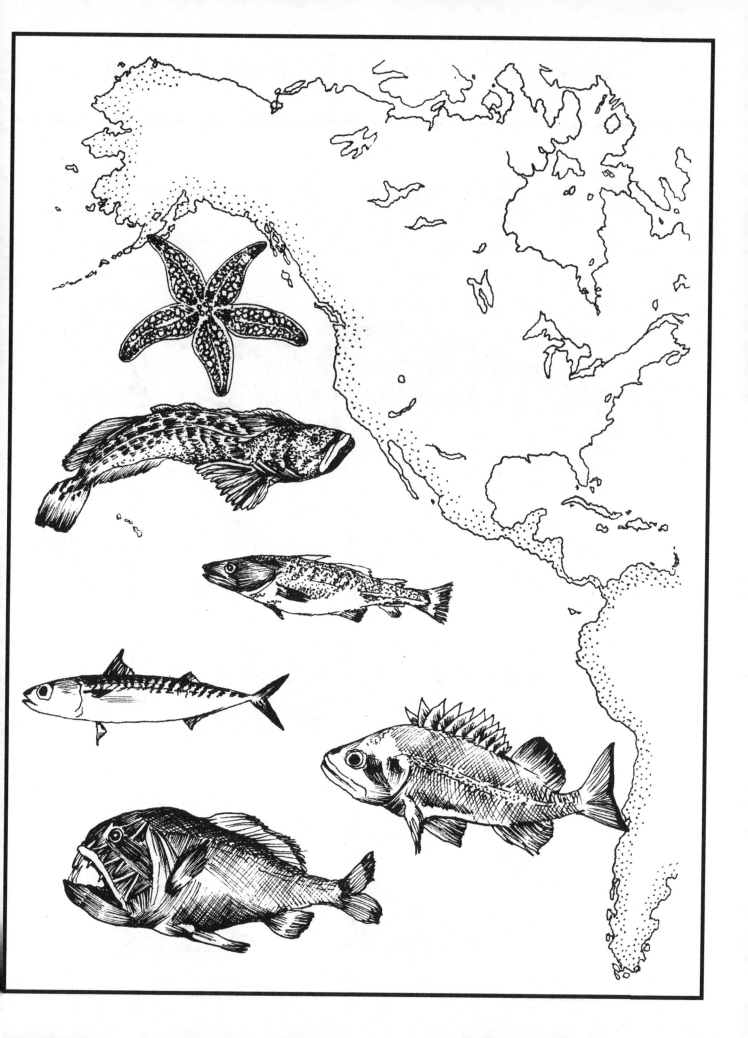

Epipelagic zone of the Pacific ocean

Find creatures that are hidden in the picture

CLIP ART

Use stickers, pictures from magazines, or print out pictures of ocean creatures from the internet and paste them on these pages.

BEACH DAY

BY ANITA AND KAYDEN KLAUSE

I wake up on a hot summer day.
It's off to the beach we go to play!
I pack my shovel, my pail, my towel,
and my camera to photograph the many seafowl.
At the beach we explore by the docks,
and find dozens of crabs hiding under the rocks.
When the tide goes out, we go and explore,
and find sand dollars, geoducks
and clams on the shore.
Then mama calls us in for a tasty treat.
We eat fresh watermelon, and it drips on my feet.
As I look out at the Pacific Ocean I see,
a large bald eagle flying towards me.

REPLACE THE ADJECTIVES AND VERBS
TO MAKE A WHOLE NEW POEM!

Add artwork to the page.

I wake up on a _____ summer day.
It's off to the beach we go to _____!
I _____ my shovel, my pail, my towel,
and my camera to photograph the many seafowl.
At the beach we _____ by the docks,
and find dozens of crabs _____ under the rocks.
When the tide goes out, we go and explore,
and _____ sand dollars, geoducks
and clams on the shore.
Then mama calls us in for a tasty treat.
We _____ fresh watermelon, and it _____ on my feet.
As I look out at the Pacific Ocean I see,
a large bald eagle _____ towards me.

COPYWORK

Copy a sentence from one of your library books.

TITLE: _____

Page#_____

_____

_____

_____

_____

_____

DRAWING TIME

Copy an illustration from one of your books.

DRAWING TIME

Copy a picture from any of your books.

ANIMAL FACTS

LINGCOD

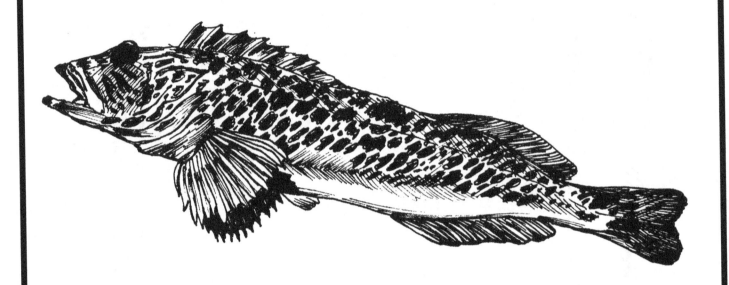

WRITE DOWN THREE FACTS ABOUT THIS ANIMAL:

1._____

_____

2._____

_____

3._____

_____

RESEARCH & DISCOVERIES

USE LIBRARY BOOKS, ENCYCLOPEDIAS OR THE INTERNET TO LEARN MORE.

Color the parts of the world where this animal lives.

DRAW MY HOME	DRAW MY FOOD	DRAW MY ENEMIES

LIGHTKEEPER'S DAUGHTER

BY JOSEPH KLAUSE

In a tower above Atlantic water,
by a window stands a lightkeeper's daughter.
Looking out for wayward Nova Scotians,
who need help in these treacherous oceans.
She sits down to rest in the candlelight,
listening to the sounds of the stormy night.
The sound of the waves on the rocks nearby,
the sound of the seabirds as they cry.
The sound of the wind
moving through the trees,
the sound of the thunder above the seas.
This is the life of the lightkeeper's daughter,
in a lighthouse above Atlantic water.

REPLACE THE ADJECTIVES AND VERBS
TO MAKE A WHOLE NEW POEM!

Add artwork to the page.

In a tower above Atlantic water,
by a window _____ a lightkeeper's daughter.
Looking out for _____ Nova Scotians,
who need help in these _____ oceans.
She sits down to _____ in the candlelight,
_____ to the sounds of the stormy night.
The sound of the waves on the rocks nearby,
the sound of the seabirds as they _____.
The sound of the wind
_____ through the trees,
the _____ of the thunder above the seas.
This is the life of the lightkeeper's daughter,
in a lighthouse above Atlantic water.

LISTENING TIME

Listen to a podcast, audio book or inspiring music.

Draw and doodle below.

I am listening to: _____

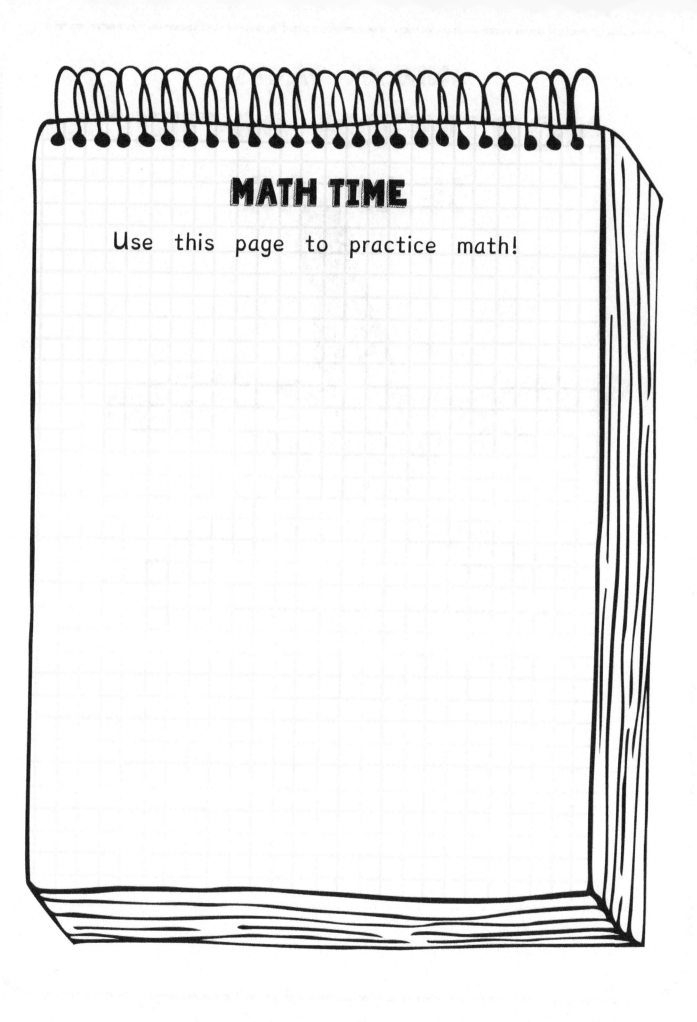

MATH TIME

Use this page to practice math!

ANIMAL FACTS
NORTHERN PACIFIC SEASTAR

WRITE DOWN THREE FACTS ABOUT THIS ANIMAL:

1._____

_____

2._____

_____

3._____

_____

RESEARCH & DISCOVERIES

USE LIBRARY BOOKS, ENCYCLOPEDIAS OR THE INTERNET TO LEARN MORE.

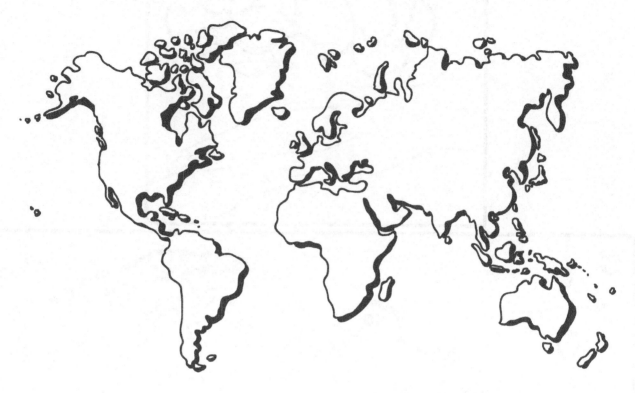

Color the parts of the world where this animal lives.

DRAW MY HOME	DRAW MY FOOD	DRAW MY ENEMIES

CREATIVE WRITING

Write a short story about these pictures.

_____

_____

_____

_____

_____

_____

_____

_____

_____

_____

_____

_____

_____

_____

_____

_____

_____

_____

_____

ANIMAL FACTS
SEA LION

WRITE DOWN THREE FACTS ABOUT THIS ANIMAL:

1._____

_____

2._____

_____

3._____

_____

RESEARCH & DISCOVERIES

USE LIBRARY BOOKS, ENCYCLOPEDIAS OR THE INTERNET TO LEARN MORE.

Color the parts of the world where this animal lives.

DRAW MY HOME	DRAW MY FOOD	DRAW MY ENEMIES

YOUR BOAT TRIP AWAITS

BY SHANNON DESMOND-SHEARN

Get your sea legs ready and follow me,
out on a boat trip over the sea.
Sunshine glistening on the water's surface,
as we're listening for the splash of a porpoise!
The captain steers the wheel ever so gently,
as we gaze at the water smiling contently.
A warm ocean breeze fills the air,
the sailboat glides through the
water without a care.
Sunbathing, Parasailing, Fishing or
Picnicking on the ocean,
which one of these strikes your
heart's devotion?
Get your sea legs ready and follow me,
your boat trip awaits by the dock at sea.

REPLACE THE ADJECTIVES AND VERBS
TO MAKE A WHOLE NEW POEM!

Add artwork to the page.

Get your sea legs ready and _____ me,
out on a boat trip over the sea.
Sunshine _____ on the water's surface,
as we're _____ for the _____ of a porpoise!
The captain _____ the wheel ever so _____,
as we _____ at the water smiling _____.
A _____ ocean breeze _____ the air,
the sailboat _____ through the
water without a care.
Sunbathing, Parasailing, Fishing or
Picnicking on the ocean,
which one of these _____ your
heart's devotion?
Get your sea legs ready and follow me,
your boat trip awaits by the dock at sea.

SPELLING TIME

Pick a Letter _____

Look in your homeschooling books for

words that start with this letter.

Write ten spelling words.

1._____

2._____

3._____

4._____

5._____

6._____

7._____

8._____

9._____

10._____

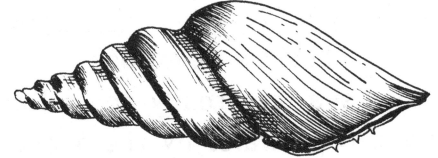

DRAWING TIME

Copy a picture from any of your books.

Mesopelagic zone of the Pacific Ocean

Practice drawing ocean creatures

MOVIE TIME

Watch a video about the ocean or ocean creatures!

TITLE:_____

RATING:

ANIMAL FACTS
PACIFIC COD

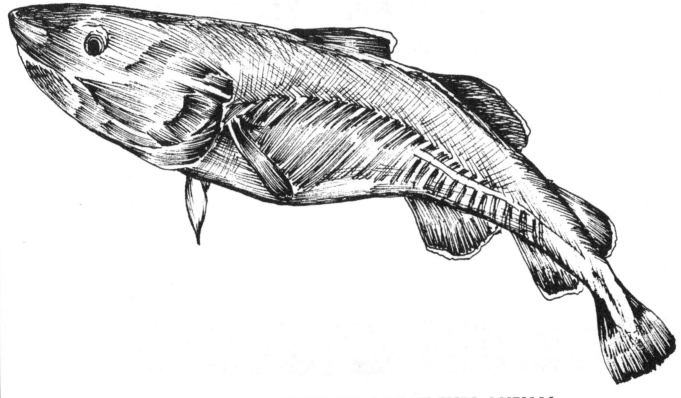

WRITE DOWN THREE FACTS ABOUT THIS ANIMAL:

1._____

_____

2._____

_____

3._____

_____

RESEARCH & DISCOVERIES

USE LIBRARY BOOKS, ENCYCLOPEDIAS OR THE INTERNET TO LEARN MORE.

Color the parts of the world where this animal lives.

| DRAW MY HOME | DRAW MY FOOD | DRAW MY ENEMIES |

CREATE A COMIC STRIP

CURSIVE WRITING PRACTICE

SPELLING TIME

Pick a Letter _____

Look in your homeschooling books for

words that start with this letter.

Write ten spelling words.

1._____

2._____

3._____

4._____

5._____

6._____

7._____

8._____

9._____

10._____

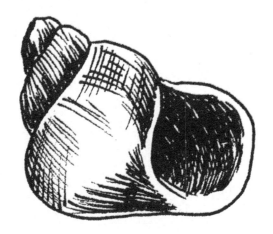

CLIP ART

Use stickers, pictures from magazines, or print out pictures of ocean creatures from the internet and paste them on these pages.

ANIMAL FACTS
TIGER SHARK

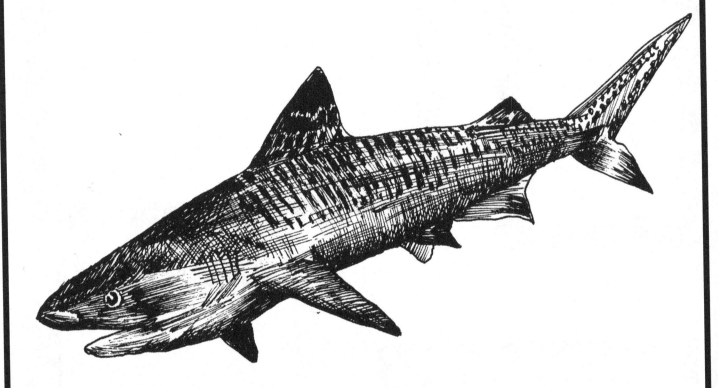

WRITE DOWN THREE FACTS ABOUT THIS ANIMAL:

1._____

_____

2._____

_____

3._____

_____

RESEARCH & DISCOVERIES

USE LIBRARY BOOKS, ENCYCLOPEDIAS OR THE INTERNET TO LEARN MORE.

Color the parts of the world where this animal lives.

DRAW MY HOME	DRAW MY FOOD	DRAW MY ENEMIES

SEAHORSES

BY LILLIAN ELLISTON

Seahorses,
swimming in the sea.
Swimming back and forth,
so gracefully.
Daddy seahorse nearby.
Mommy near them too.
Watching all their babies swimming happily in
the great big blue.

REPLACE THE ADJECTIVES AND VERBS TO MAKE A WHOLE NEW POEM!

Add artwork to the page.

Seahorses,
_____ in the sea.
Swimming back and forth,
so _____ .
Daddy seahorse nearby.
Mommy near them too.
_____ all their babies swimming _____ in the great _____ blue.

READING TIME

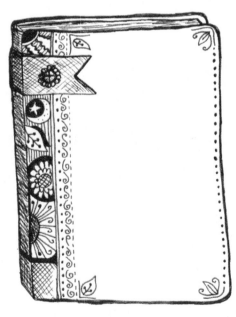

Write and draw about
what you are reading.

MATH TIME

Use this page to practice math!

CREATE A COMIC STRIP

a B C D E F G

H I J K L M

N O P Q R S T

U V W X Y Z

a b c d e f g h

i j k l m n o p

q r s t u v w x

y z 1 2 3 4 5 6 7 8 9 0

CURSIVE WRITING PRACTICE

ANIMAL FACTS
CHUB MACKEREL

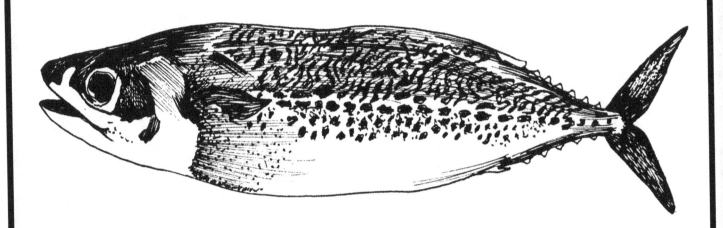

WRITE DOWN THREE FACTS ABOUT THIS ANIMAL:

1._____

_____

2._____

_____

3._____

_____

RESEARCH & DISCOVERIES

USE LIBRARY BOOKS, ENCYCLOPEDIAS OR THE INTERNET TO LEARN MORE.

Color the parts of the world where this animal lives.

DRAW MY HOME	DRAW MY FOOD	DRAW MY ENEMIES

LITTLE SEAHORSE

BY SHANNON AND ISABELLE SHEARN

Little Seahorse,
you're so special to me,
floating adrift in the deep blue sea.
The ocean current guides you to a patch of seaweeds.
Your tail grasps the seagrass & curls tight.
Hold on little seahorse,
you're such a delight!
Those brilliant colors & markings catch my eye,
while the coral reef provides shelter for your baby
seahorse "fry".
Born from a father seahorse,
so truly unique!
Little seahorse with your equine physique!

REPLACE THE ADJECTIVES AND VERBS
TO MAKE A WHOLE NEW POEM!

Add artwork to the page.

Little Seahorse,
you're so _____ to me,
_____ adrift in the deep _____ sea.
The ocean current _____ you to a
patch of seaweeds.
Your tail _____ the seagrass & curls tight.
Hold on _____ seahorse,
you're such a _____ !
Those _____ colors & markings catch my eye,
while the coral reef provides shelter for your baby
seahorse "fry".
Born from a father seahorse,
so truly unique!
Little seahorse with your equine physique!

MATH TIME

Use this page to practice math!

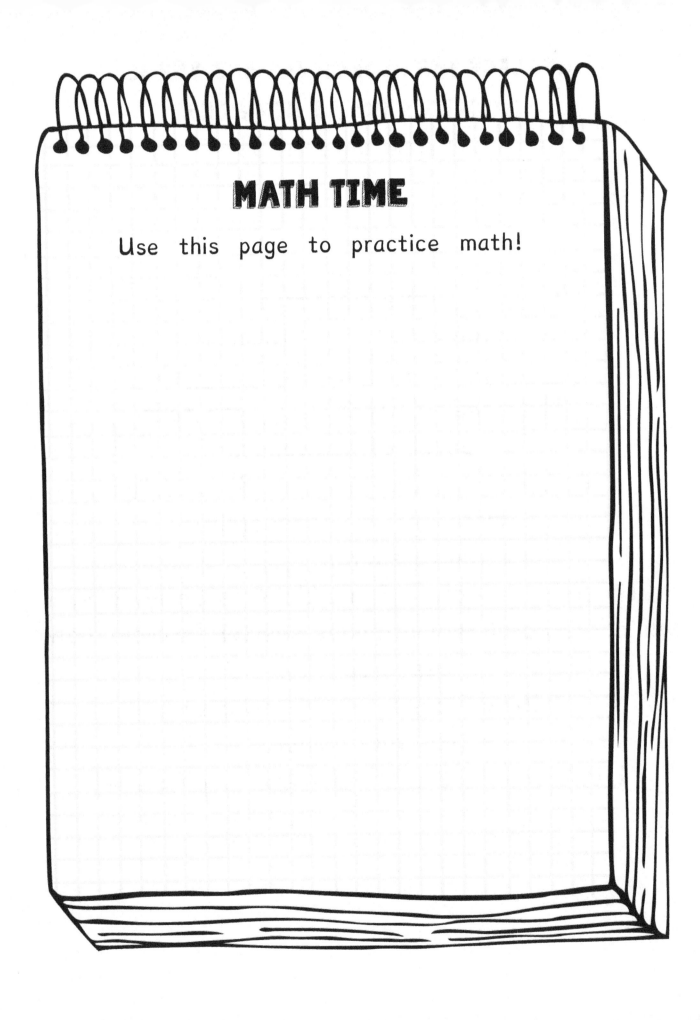

LISTENING TIME

Listen to a podcast, audio book or inspiring music.

Draw and doodle below.

I am listening to: _____

Bathypelagic zone of the Pacific Ocean

Find creatures that are hidden in the picture

DRAWING TIME

Copy a picture from any of your books.

ANIMAL FACTS
VAMPIRE SQUID

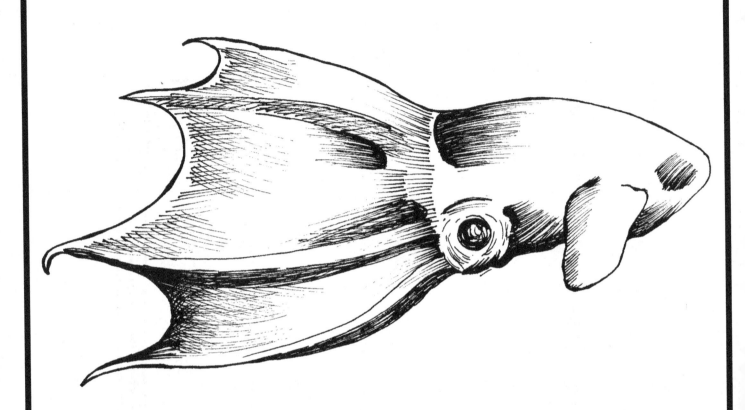

WRITE DOWN THREE FACTS ABOUT THIS ANIMAL:

1._____

_____

2._____

_____

3._____

_____

RESEARCH & DISCOVERIES

USE LIBRARY BOOKS, ENCYCLOPEDIAS OR THE INTERNET TO LEARN MORE.

Color the parts of the world where this animal lives.

DRAW MY HOME	DRAW MY FOOD	DRAW MY ENEMIES

OCEAN ADVENTURES

BY LALENE HOBBS

Ocean so blue, sky so clear.
Sharks losing teeth every year:
you can find as a souvenir.
Jellyfish with their sting you will find
that you're in pain,
but you will come to the ocean again and again.
Sand and shells mix so well,
making music in sync.
Listen to the waves playing a tune.
Manatees so gentle get scratches
and cuts from boats above.
The ocean view with the sun is what I love.

REPLACE THE ADJECTIVES AND VERBS TO MAKE A WHOLE NEW POEM!

Add artwork to the page.

Ocean so _____, sky so _____.
Sharks _____ teeth every year:
you can find as a souvenir.
Jellyfish with their sting you will _____
that you're in pain,
but you will come to the ocean again and again.
Sand and shells mix so well,
_____ music in sync.
_____ to the waves _____ a tune.
Manatees so _____ get scratches
and cuts from boats above.
The ocean view with the sun is what I love.

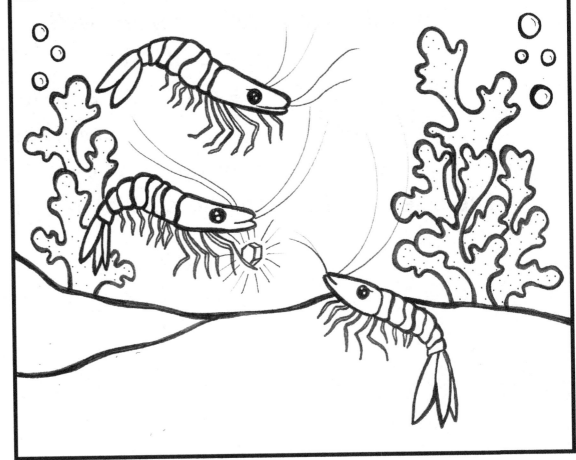

CREATIVE WRITING

Write a short story about these pictures.

_____

_____

_____

_____

_____

_____

_____

_____

_____

_____

_____

_____

_____

_____

_____

_____

_____

_____

_____

MOVIE TIME

Watch a video about the ocean or ocean creatures!

TITLE:_____

COPYWORK

Copy a sentence from one of your library books.

TITLE: _____

Page#_____

_____

_____

_____

_____

_____

DRAWING TIME

Copy an illustration from one of your books.

ANIMAL FACTS
ROCKFISH

WRITE DOWN THREE FACTS ABOUT THIS ANIMAL:

1._____

_____

2._____

_____

3._____

_____

RESEARCH & DISCOVERIES

USE LIBRARY BOOKS, ENCYCLOPEDIAS OR THE INTERNET TO LEARN MORE.

Color the parts of the world where this animal lives.

DRAW MY HOME	DRAW MY FOOD	DRAW MY ENEMIES

OCEAN

BY STEPHANIE JACOBS

The ocean so big,
the whales are too.
So much to discover,
me and you.
The fish so exotic,
their species are many.
Their colors, their sizes,
their ways, so friendly.
Echolocation,
the dolphins, they speak,
of wonder and love,
with each little squeak.
The ocean is vast,
the ocean is blue,
so much to discover,
me and you.

REPLACE THE ADJECTIVES AND VERBS TO MAKE A WHOLE NEW POEM!

Add artwork to the page.

The ocean so _____,
the whales are too.
So much to discover,
me and you.
The fish so _____,
their species are many.
Their colors, their sizes,
their ways, so _____.
Echolocation,
the dolphins, they speak,
of wonder and love,
with each little squeak.
The ocean is _____,
the ocean is _____,
so much to discover,
me and you.

Today I will
read for

15 30 45 60

MINUTES

READING
TIME

Write and draw about
what you are reading.

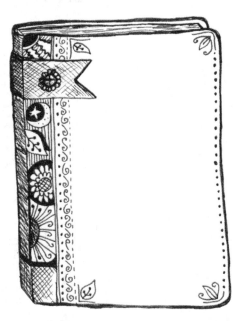

MATH TIME

Use this page to practice math!

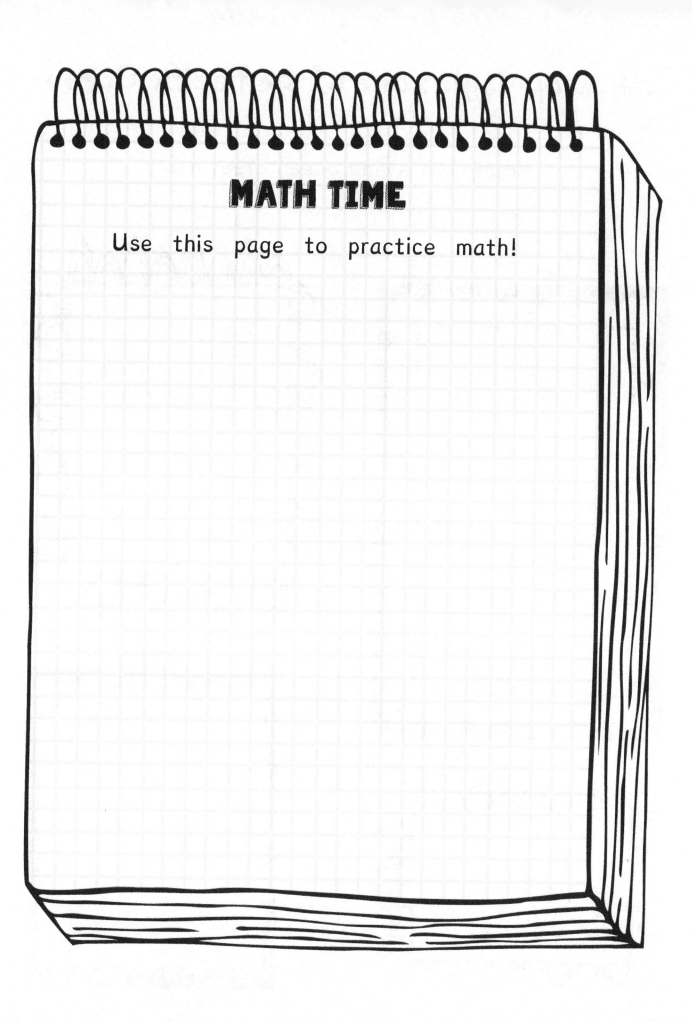

Abyssopelagic zone of the Pacific Ocean

Practice drawing ocean creatures

SPELLING TIME

Pick a Letter _____

Look in your homeschooling books for
words that start with this letter.
Write ten spelling words.

1. _____
2. _____
3. _____
4. _____
5. _____
6. _____
7. _____
8. _____
9. _____
10. _____

ANIMAL FACTS
TUBE WORMS

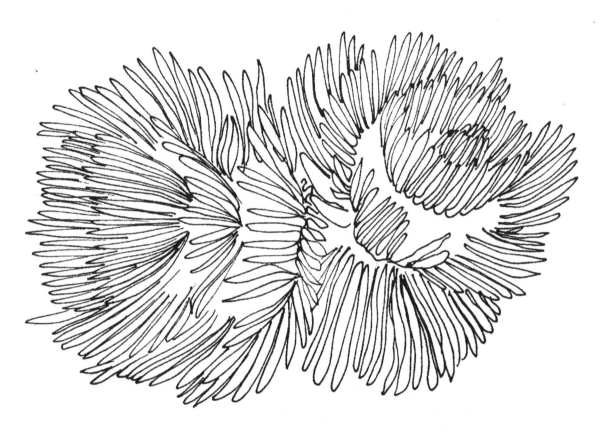

WRITE DOWN THREE FACTS ABOUT THIS ANIMAL:

1._____

_____

2._____

_____

3._____

_____

RESEARCH & DISCOVERIES

USE LIBRARY BOOKS, ENCYCLOPEDIAS OR THE INTERNET TO LEARN MORE.

Color the parts of the world where this animal lives.

DRAW MY HOME	DRAW MY FOOD	DRAW MY ENEMIES

a B C D E F G

H I J K L M

N O P Q R S T

U V W X Y Z

a b c d e f g h

i j k l m n o p

q r s t u v w x

y z 1 2 3 4 5 6 7 8 9 0

CURSIVE WRITING PRACTICE

CLIP ART

Use stickers, pictures from magazines, or print out pictures of ocean creatures from the internet and paste them on these pages.

DRAWING TIME

Copy a picture from any of your books.

ANIMAL FACTS
FANGTOOTH

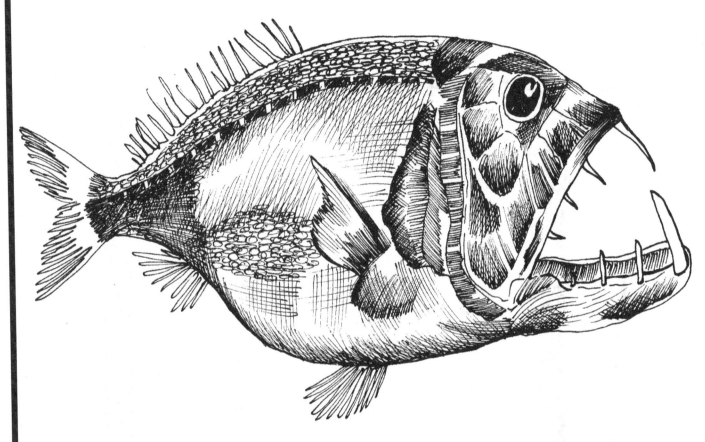

WRITE DOWN THREE FACTS ABOUT THIS ANIMAL:

1._____

_____

2._____

_____

3._____

_____

RESEARCH & DISCOVERIES

USE LIBRARY BOOKS, ENCYCLOPEDIAS OR THE INTERNET TO LEARN MORE.

Color the parts of the world where this animal lives.

DRAW MY HOME

DRAW MY FOOD

DRAW MY ENEMIES

SPELLING TIME

Pick a Letter _____

Look in your homeschooling books for

words that start with this letter.

Write ten spelling words.

1._____

2._____

3._____

4._____

5._____

6._____

7._____

8._____

9._____

10._____

MOVIE TIME

Watch a video about the ocean or ocean creatures!

TITLE:_____

RATING:

Draw Your Favorite Scenes:

ALL ABOUT OCEANS

CREATIVE WRITING & RESEARCH

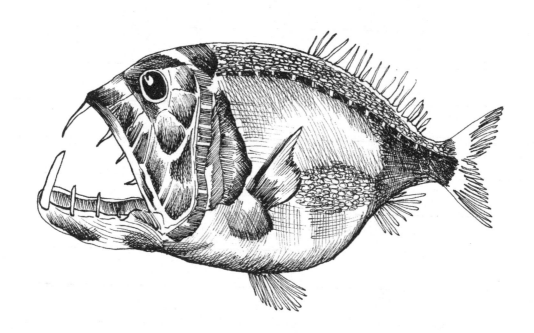

Add your own stories, poems,
research, copywork or journal entries
to the following pages.

CREATIVE WRITING & RESEARCH

Use this photo as inspiration for a short story or poem.

_____

_____

_____

_____

_____

_____

_____

_____

_____

_____

_____

_____

_____

_____

_____

_____

_____

_____

_____

CREATIVE WRITING & RESEARCH

Use this photo as inspiration for a short story or poem.

_____

_____

_____

_____

_____

_____

_____

_____

_____

_____

_____

_____

_____

_____

_____

_____

_____

_____

CREATIVE WRITING & RESEARCH

Use this photo as inspiration for a short story or poem.

_____

_____

_____

_____

_____

_____

_____

_____

_____

_____

_____

_____

_____

_____

_____

_____

_____

CREATIVE WRITING & RESEARCH

Use this photo as inspiration for a short story or poem.

_____

_____

_____

_____

_____

_____

_____

_____

_____

_____

_____

_____

_____

_____

_____

_____

_____

_____

_____

CREATIVE WRITING & RESEARCH

Use this photo as inspiration for a short story or poem.

_____

_____

_____

_____

_____

_____

_____

_____

_____

_____

_____

_____

_____

_____

_____

_____

_____

_____

CREATIVE WRITING & RESEARCH

Use this photo as inspiration for a short story or poem.

_____

_____

_____

_____

_____

_____

_____

_____

_____

_____

_____

_____

_____

_____

_____

_____

CREATIVE WRITING & RESEARCH

Use this photo as inspiration for a short story or poem.

_____

_____

_____

_____

_____

_____

_____

_____

_____

_____

_____

_____

_____

_____

_____

_____

_____

_____

_____

CREATIVE WRITING & RESEARCH

Use this photo as inspiration for a short story or poem.

_____

_____

_____

_____

_____

_____

_____

_____

_____

_____

_____

_____

_____

_____

_____

_____

_____

_____

CREATIVE WRITING & RESEARCH

Use this photo as inspiration for a short story or poem.

_____

_____

_____

_____

_____

_____

_____

_____

_____

_____

_____

_____

_____

_____

_____

_____

_____

CREATIVE WRITING & RESEARCH

Use this photo as inspiration for a short story or poem.

_____

_____

_____

_____

_____

_____

_____

_____

_____

_____

_____

_____

_____

_____

_____

_____

_____

_____

CREATIVE WRITING & RESEARCH

Use this photo as inspiration for a short story or poem.

_____

_____

_____

_____

_____

_____

_____

_____

_____

_____

_____

_____

_____

_____

_____

_____

_____

_____

CREATIVE WRITING & RESEARCH

Use this photo as inspiration for a short story or poem.

_____

_____

_____

_____

_____

_____

_____

_____

_____

_____

_____

_____

_____

_____

_____

_____

_____

CREATIVE WRITING & RESEARCH

Use this photo as inspiration for a short story or poem.

_____

_____

_____

_____

_____

_____

_____

_____

_____

_____

_____

_____

_____

_____

_____

_____

_____

CREATIVE WRITING & RESEARCH

Use this photo as inspiration for a short story or poem.

_____

_____

_____

_____

_____

_____

_____

_____

_____

_____

_____

_____

_____

_____

_____

_____

_____

CREATIVE WRITING & RESEARCH

Use this photo as inspiration for a short story or poem.

_____

_____

_____

_____

_____

_____

_____

_____

_____

_____

_____

_____

_____

_____

_____

_____

CREATIVE WRITING & RESEARCH

Use this photo as inspiration for a short story or poem.

_____

_____

_____

_____

_____

_____

_____

_____

_____

_____

_____

_____

_____

_____

_____

_____

_____

_____

_____

CREATIVE WRITING & RESEARCH

Use this photo as inspiration for a short story or poem.

_____

_____

_____

_____

_____

_____

_____

_____

_____

_____

_____

_____

_____

_____

_____

_____

_____

CREATIVE WRITING & RESEARCH

Use this photo as inspiration for a short story or poem.

_____

_____

_____

_____

_____

_____

_____

_____

_____

_____

_____

_____

_____

_____

_____

_____

_____

_____

CREATIVE WRITING & RESEARCH

Use this photo as inspiration for a short story or poem.

_____

_____

_____

_____

_____

_____

_____

_____

_____

_____

_____

_____

_____

_____

_____

_____

_____

_____

Do It Yourself

HOMESCHOOL

JOURNALS

Copyright Information

Contact Us:

The Thinking Tree LLC

317.622.8852 PHONE (Dial +1 outside of the USA) 267.712.7889 FAX

FunSchoolingBooks.com